The Radio Amateur's Digital Communications Handbook

The Radio Amateur's Digital Communications Handbook

Jonathan L. Mayo, KR3T

TAB Books
Division of McGraw-Hill, Inc.
Blue Ridge Summit, PA 17294-0850

Notices

Apple IIe, Macintosh®	Apple Computer Co. ProDOS
AX.25	pending service mark of ARRL
AMSAT®	The Radio Amateur Satellite Corporation
CP/M™	Digital Research Corporation
HAYES®	Hayes Corporation
IBM™	International Business Machines Corporation
IBM PC®	International Business Machines
MS-DOS™	Microsoft Corporation
NOVRAM™	Xicor
Teletype	Teletype Corporation
TRS-80®	Tandy Corporation
UNIX™	Bell Labs
Xerox 820™	Xerox Corporation
Z-80™	Zilog Corporation

FIRST EDITION
SECOND PRINTING

Library of Congress Cataloging-in-Publication Data

Mayo, Jonathan L.
The radio amateur's digital communications handbook / by Jonathan
L. Mayo.
p.   cm.
Includes index.
ISBN 0-8306-8362-3   ISBN 0-8306-3362-6 (pbk.)
1. Digital communications—Amateurs' manuals.   2. Radio—Amateurs'
manuals.   I. Title.
TK9956.M366   1992

621.384—dc20   91-31798
                                                                         CIP

Acquisitions Editor: Roland Phelps
Book Editor: Suzanne L. Cheatle
Managing Editor: Sandra L. Johnson
Director of Production: Katherine G. Brown
Book Design: Jaclyn J. Boone
Paperbound Cover Design: Graphics Plus, Hanover, PA.   LHP3
Paperbound Cover Photograph: Brent Blair Photography, Harrisburg, PA   3362

To family and friends

Contents

Acknowledgments

THE BOOK YOU ARE HOLDING NOW IS DIRECTLY ATTRIBUTABLE TO THE SUCCESS of *The Packet Radio Handbook*, my first amateur radio book. *TPRH*, with its multiple printings and editions, has proven that a substantial market exists for amateur radio books of this type. Readers such as you who purchase books determine what type and kind of books get published. Thanks to you, I had the opportunity to write this one. I hope you enjoy it, and thank you for purchasing a copy.

Many people and organizations helped me produce this book by providing information. I would like to take this opportunity to thank them and acknowledge their participation: AMSAT, ARRL, Phil Anderson and Lori Elliott of Kantronics, Gil Boelke and Deborah Sanders of GLB, Andrew Demartini of DRSI, Steve Fine of S. Fine Software, Ted Harris, Lyle Johnson of TAPR, Mike Lamb and John Downing of AEA, Doug Lockhart of VADCG, Hank Oredson, Harold Price, Gwyn Reedy of Pac-Comm, Eddie Richey of MFJ, Brooks Van Pelt of L.L. Grace, and Wayne Wilson of Heathkit. My apologies to anyone I might have missed.

I would also like to thank Brint Rutherford, Roland Phelps, and Ray Collins again for their help with *TPRH*. This time around, thanks are once again due to Roland Phelps for his enthusiastic support of this book.

Introduction

THE WORLD OF AMATEUR RADIO DIGITAL COMMUNICATIONS IS AS DIVERSE AS IT IS interesting. A wide variety of modes exist for most any operating situation. However, learning about the modes—their strengths, weaknesses, and comparative value— can be difficult. Today's multimode digital controllers, which contain several digital modes in one convenient unit, have altered the information needs of amateurs.

Previously, amateurs commonly purchased or built one interface for each mode they operated. This step-by-step approach allowed them time to gather information on individual modes as they upgraded their stations. But the amateur who purchases a multimode interface needs a one-stop source of thorough information on all the modes. Too often, the interface's manual assumes familiarity with the digital modes and is of little help to users who are new to a particular mode.

In this book's 10 chapters and numerous appendices, all the major digital modes are introduced and explained. CW, Baudot RTTY, ASCII RTTY, AMTOR, packet, SSTV, and fax—it's all here—plus operating information on HF, VHF, UHF, and satellite. This book will help you unlock the potential of your digital station and, hopefully, provide you with additional enjoyment.

Chapter 1 starts the book off with an introduction to the basic concepts of digital communications. The history of the various modes is covered in chapter 2. Chapters 3 through 7 explain the specifics of the major modes. Setting up a digital station is covered in chapter 8, and chapter 9 reviews most of the available digital interfaces and accessories to help you make informed purchase decisions. Finally, chapter 10 looks ahead to future developments.

A wide variety of related information is included in the seven appendices—from code charts to operating frequencies. The bibliography offers sources of additional information, and the glossary should help you with unfamiliar terms. All in all, *The Radio Amateur's Digital Communications Handbook* is a complete source for comprehensive information on digital communications in amateur radio.

Because all digital modes share many common aspects, I designed this book to be read through completely at least once. This method will give you an overview of the technology of digital communications, since I did not feel it necessary to repeat basic information throughout each chapter. If you are primarily interested in one particular mode, read that chapter and then check the index to see if any related information is contained in other chapters.

I hope you find *The Radio Amateur's Digital Communications Handbook* to be useful, informative, and entertaining.

1
Digital communications basics

WELCOME TO THE EXCITING WORLD OF DIGITAL COMMUNICATIONS. AS YOU MIGHT already know or will soon discover, the world of digital communications is expansive and dynamic, as well as a lot of fun. Although digital communications has been a part of amateur radio since its beginnings, interest in digital communications has grown rapidly over the past decade.

The advent and subsequent expansion of packet radio has done much to spur this interest in digital communications. Today, units that are capable of operating all of the major digital modes are available. These multimode interfaces have brought about a revolution in amateur radio digital communications. No longer are operators required to purchase additional equipment for each mode they want to work.

In the following chapters, I examine each of the major digital modes in detail. Later chapters cover setting up a digital communications station and available equipment and accessories, as well as developments to watch in the future. For now, however, get acquainted with the basics of digital communications.

Fundamentals

In a digital communications system like radioteletype (RTTY) or packet, information is transmitted and received in *digital form*; that is, each piece of information is represented by a digital code. The digital code is made up of one or more elements. These elements can have different states or levels. For example, our decimal number system is a digital code in which each element is one of 10 possible levels (0 to 9). The number 100 is represented by the code 100 in our decimal system of 10 levels.

The binary system has only two states, represented by a 1 or 0. Thus, each element can have only two levels. Each element is called a *binary digit* or bit. The decimal number 100 is represented by the binary code 1100100.

The binary system, with two states or levels, is used extensively in digital systems and communications. The two states can be represented in electronic equipment by two different voltages, two different currents, or two different frequencies. In most cases, a multiple-state system, with three or more levels, is not used because of the increased sensitivity and calibration of the electronics that would be required to differentiate between more than two levels. For example, it is much easier to construct equipment that can differentiate between two voltage levels, one positive and one negative, than to build equipment that can differentiate between three, four, or more voltage levels.

In order to represent more than two different conditions using the binary system, bits must be combined to increase the number of possible corresponding conditions. For example, 1 bit is sufficient to indicate if a light is on or off, or if a door is open or closed (Fig. 1-1). However, to represent more complex concepts, such as the number system or alphabet, several bits are combined. If 2 bits are combined, 4 different conditions can be indicated. The total number of possible combinations can be found by raising 2 to the power of the number of bits that have been combined (ie. 2•2=4, 2•2•2=8). Because the alphabet has 26 different characters, 5 bits must be combined for a total of 32 different possible characters. To include the numerals 0 to 9, uppercase and lowercase characters, and some punctuation, a minimum of 7 bits are needed, for a total of 128 possible combinations.

Getting back to the number 100, 7 bits must be combined to represent the number in binary. Six bits are too few (only 64 possible combinations), and 7 bits are too many (128 possible combinations), so we must choose the larger. Although it is rel-

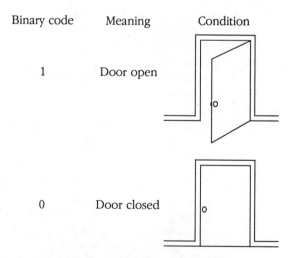

Binary code	Meaning	Condition
1	Door open	
0	Door closed	

Fig. 1-1. One binary digit (bit) can be used to differentiate between two different states, such as an open and closed door as shown.

atively easy to convert between binary and decimal, this process is not covered in this book. Some computer books contain a conversion table in their appendices, and most scientific calculators can do base conversions with ease.

Binary codes

In digital communications, information is transferred as follows: Each piece of information is assigned a binary combination, which is transmitted to the receiving station(s), where it is reassigned with its original value, provided the sending station and receiving station are following the same binary combination assignment (code). This information is usually characters in text; however, it can also be digitized pictures, voice, or anything else that can be broken down into discrete pieces of data (Fig. 1-2).

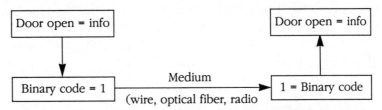

Fig. 1-2. To transfer the condition of the door to another station, the state of the door is noted as information, then the binary representation is sent to the other station. At the receiving station, the binary representation is reassigned the same information.

Several standardized codes are in use today for the transfer of text data. Some of them might be familiar to you: American Standard Code for Information Interchange (ASCII), Expanded Binary Coded Decimal Interchange Code (EBCDIC), Baudot, and Murray. Charts of the Morse, Baudot, and ASCII codes are contained in the appendices.

Once these binary combinations are generated—whether by a mechanical teleprinter, microcomputer, or some other device—they are often sent to a modem (*mo*dulator *dem*odulator). This device generates (modulates) tones (frequencies), which correspond to the state of each bit for transmission over an analog medium, such as a radio link or telephone line.

The two tones are given special names. The tone corresponding to the binary 1 is called the *mark*, and the tone corresponding to the binary 0 is called the *space*. This terminology dates back to the early days of telegraphy when an automatic receiving device would lower a pen on a strip of paper when a signal was present, making a mark. Of course, when there was no signal, the pen would not touch the paper and a space would result.

These tones are then transmitted by a radio transmitter or carried via cable to the receiver(s), where the tones are converted back into digital signals (demodulated) by another modem.

A transmission medium in which two separate signals can be transmitted in opposite directions at the same time is known as a *full-duplex channel* (i.e., two stations can transmit to each other at the same time). A transmission medium in which two separate signals can be transmitted in opposite directions but only one signal can be transmitted at a time in either direction is known as a *half-duplex channel* (i.e., two stations can transmit to each other but not at the same time). A transmission medium in which only one signal can be transmitted at a time in only one direction is known as a *simplex channel* (i.e., one of two station transmits and the other receives). A half-duplex channel can be considered a simplex channel that can reverse direction between stations.

Modes of digital communication

One of the questions most frequently asked about amateur radio digital communications is which mode is the best. As you'll soon discover, there is no one best mode. The ideal situation is to be able to operate all of the following modes: Continuous Wave (CW), Baudot RTTY, ASCII RTTY, Amateur Teletype Over Radio (AMTOR), and packet. This section discusses the capabilities of each of these digital communication systems. This discussion should give you a good understanding of the virtues of each mode.

CW

CW is the oldest form of digital communications. It uses an uneven form of coding, usually the Morse code. In an uneven code, the number of elements that make up each character are not equal; thus, some characters have more elements than others. Morse code contains most characters needed for communications and requires very simple equipment for transmission and reception.

Since the advent of computerized keyboards and decoders, CW can be sent very quickly. However, the slightest bit of interference or imperfect sending can reduce the decoder's ability to accurately copy the code.

Compared to other forms of digital communications, CW leaves a lot to be desired. On the plus side, CW is the only form of digital coding that can be easily copied by ear without the aid of decoding equipment.

Baudot RTTY

Baudot RTTY uses an even form of coding known as the Baudot (or Murray) code. In the Baudot code, each character is made up of 5 mark and space elements (bits). However, there are only 32 possible combinations using a 5-level code. Therefore, Baudot includes 2 different character sets: figures and letters. The character sets are alternated as needed.

Baudot RTTY operation usually takes place at speeds of 45, 50, or 75 baud using either solid state equipment or mechanical teleprinters (Fig. 1-3). In most cases, the baud rate is roughly equal to the number of elements (bits) sent per second. A more accurate definition of baud will be presented later.

ASCII RTTY

ASCII RTTY was first legalized in 1980 by the FCC for amateur use in the United States in response to the wide proliferation of computer equipment, which uses the

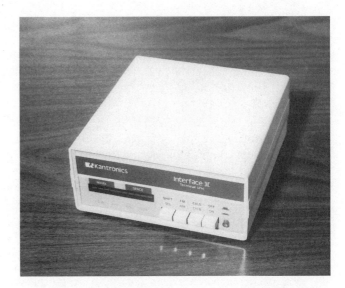

Fig. 1-3. The Kantronics Interface II, an RTTY terminal unit.

7-element ASCII code. Its primary advantages over Baudot RTTY are its speed (usually 110 or 300 baud) and its 128 possible characters. Solid state equipment is usually used for ASCII operation, as shown in Fig. 1-4, but mechanical teleprinters also can be used. In operation, ASCII RTTY is very similar to Baudot RTTY except for the coding used.

AMTOR

AMTOR introduced two new dimensions to amateur RTTY communications: error checking and time diversity. These two topics are covered in greater detail in later sections. AMTOR was first legalized for amateur use in 1983.

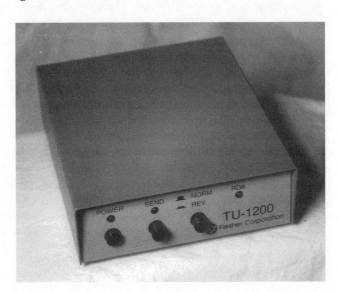

Fig. 1-4. The Flesher TU-1200 modem.

AMTOR uses a special even coding in which there is a constant ratio of mark and space elements. If the received character does not have the proper ratio, it is presumed erroneous. AMTOR operates at 100 baud and, because of the error checking, is much more reliable than standard Baudot or ASCII RTTY.

Packet

Packet is the most advanced form of digital communications available to radio amateurs. The primary advantages of packet radio are speed, networking, error checking, and efficient use of frequency space.

Packet radio operates using a standard digital communications networking technique known as Carrier Sense Multiple Access with Collision Detection (CSMA/CD). Put simply, a packet station will not transmit when the frequency is occupied. It waits until the frequency is clear and then transmits a short burst of information. Because packet transmissions are very short, many packet stations can be on the same frequency without interfering with each other. A line of text that takes 30 seconds to type can be transmitted in a fraction of a second.

Most packet activity today is at 1,200 baud on the VHF bands and 300 baud on HF. As modem technology advances, packet will be operating routinely at 9,600 baud and up on VHF.

Packet's error-checking follows the high-level data link control (HDLC) format. The data entered by the user is grouped together in bundles of (usually) 128 characters. The binary digits (bits) that compose the data and any other information to be transmitted (such as the sending and receiving stations' callsigns) are put through an extensive polynomial expression and a number unique to the specific data being transmitted in generated. This number is known as the frame check sequence (FCS). The FCS is sent along with the data. When the receiving station gets the data and the FCS, it recomputes the FCS using the same expression and compares it with the one received with the data.

If the two FCSs match, the data is assumed to be error-free and an acknowledgment (ACK) is sent to the receiving station. If they do not match, the data was not received exactly as the transmitting station sent it, so the receiving station ignores the transmission. The transmitting station retransmits the data after a period of time.

Of course, for all this to work, the two stations must be using compatible equipment (as with all forms of digital communications) and the same protocols. The equipment in packet radio consists mainly of the Terminal Node Controller (TNC), as shown in Fig. 1-5. The two TNCs can be of different manufacture, but they must use the same protocol.

Protocols define the format of the information sent. The protocol organizes the information to be transmitted into frames. A protocol also defines what steps are to be taken by the TNC under different circumstances. Networking procedures are another area that the protocol defines.

The digital communications station

The basic digital communications station is composed of four main components: the terminal/computer, a digital interface unit, a modem, and a transceiver (Fig. 1-5).

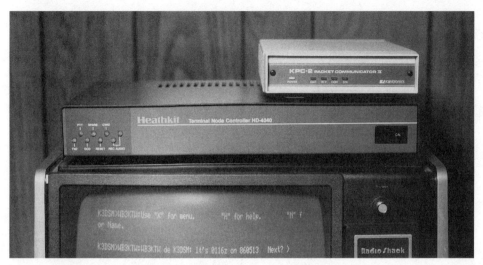

Fig. 1-5. Two amateur packet radio TNCs—a Heathkit HD-4040 and a Kantronics KPC-2.

The digital interface unit can take a variety of forms, from a simple RTTY-only interface to a packet TNC to a multimode unit. RTTY-only interfaces are known as terminal units (TUs). The name terminal node controller (TNC) was derived from its use in packet communications networks. Multimode units typically include all the features and capabilities of RTTY TUs and packet TNCs.

The digital interface unit is the heart of a digital communications station. The digital interface organizes and controls the transmission and reception of the data. Chapter 9 covers many of the available digital interfaces. You'll learn much more about their properties in later chapters.

The other components of a digital communications station are the terminal and the radio transceiver. The choice of a terminal system is discussed in chapter 8. The transceiver is usually a modern multiband HF rig and a two-meter FM rig for VHF packet use.

Setting up a digital communications station varies greatly in cost depending on what equipment is needed and what kind is acquired. A complete system starting from scratch could cost from as little as $300 up to more than $2000. If you already have a computer or terminal and a transceiver, the cost approximates $150 to $350.

Integrated circuits

In order to fully understand digital communications, it is helpful to have some understanding of integrated circuits and computer systems. Integrated circuits (ICs) have truly revolutionized electronics over the past two decades. Without ICs, it is safe to assume that most of the electronic devices we have today would not have been developed.

Integrated circuits are easy to recognize. They are usually small rectangular chips made from a black plastic material with metallic leads coming out the sides. But there is much more to an IC than this. Sealed in the plastic housing is a miniature square of silicon material measuring a few millimeters on each edge. Etched on this chip of silicon are the electronic circuits that determine the function of the IC.

Typical ICs consist of many transistors and gates. Memory chips often contain hundreds of thousands of transistors. There are 6 main gates: AND, OR, XOR, NAND, NOR, and Inverter. These gates are designed to carry out the rules of Boolean algebra, which is based on the binary system. Each gate gives a different result depending on the combination of bits applied to them. (This book won't go into detail on how each gate specifically operates or how different types of gate circuits are designed.)

The construction of integrated circuits is a processing marvel. Successive layers of resists, dopants, metals, and other materials are applied to a silicon wafer to develop the desired circuits. When all the layers are finished, the wafer is broken into hundreds of chips and tiny wires are attached to the inputs and outputs of the chip. The chip is then sealed in plastic with the tiny input and output wires attached to the metal leads sticking out of the plastic.

ICs have been designed to handle almost any desired digital task from central processing units (CPUs), to memory, to multiplexers and so on. Were you to open the case of any computer, you would see rows of ICs covering the circuit boards, each with a specific job to do. However, ICs do not work alone. They must have support components to define and regulate their operation. These support components consist of connecting circuits, resistors, capacitors, crystals, and so forth.

Microcomputer systems

With the advance of the microcomputer revolution, more and more amateur radio operators have one or more micros performing a variety of functions in the ham shack. Whether or not you decide to use a microcomputer as a communications terminal in your packet station, it is helpful to know and understand a little about microcomputer systems because they are in such wide use in digital communications.

Microcomputer systems are made up of two major components: hardware and software. Hardware is what most people visualize when they think of microcomputers. Some examples of hardware are physical devices such as cathode ray tubes (CRTs), keyboards, disk drives, printers, modems, TNCs, and their associated circuitry (Figs. 1-6 and 1-7). Before going any further, let's take a look at what makes up a microcomputer.

A basic microcomputer is actually composed of only four different sections: input, CPU, memory, and output. *Input* can take the form of a keyboard, disk drive, or anything else that allows for the input (entry) of information into the computer. The CPU is the brains of a computer. It manages the flow of information to and from the other components and performs arithmetic operations.

Memory is used for the storage of data and programs. It can be written to and read from (as with RAM, which stands for random access memory); however, some

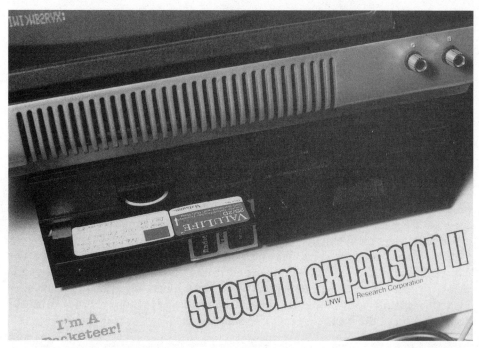

Fig. 1-6. Two 5.25-inch disk drives.

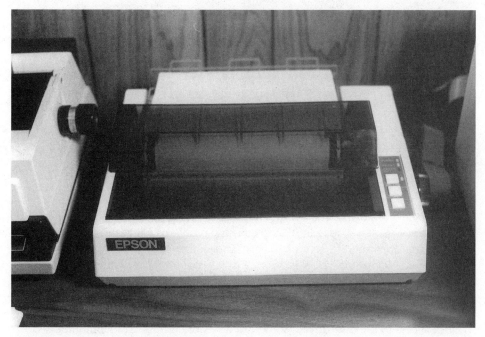

Fig. 1-7. An Epson MX-80 printer.

forms of memory cannot be written to once initially programmed (like ROM, read-only memory).

Output is where the CPU directs any information to be sent to the user or for storage on an external device. Some examples of output are display monitors, disk drives, and printers.

You might have noticed that disk drives are listed as examples of both input and output. This is perfectly correct, since some devices are used for both storage and retrieval. These devices fall under the header of *input and output (I/O)*. But all this hardware is useless for its intended function without software. An apt analogy would be a car that is full of gas and is ready to go but that has no driver.

Software tells the hardware what to do and how to do it. It is simply a list of instructions telling the computer how to accomplish a task. Software comes in many different forms and on various *media*. A *medium* is the physical device on which the software instructions are stored. Some typical microcomputer storage devices include permanent memory (ROM), cassettes, and most commonly, floppy disks (Fig. 1-8). Software stored on permanent memory chips is usually called *firmware* and can be found built into the computer and in plug-in cartridges. Most often rudimentary programs such as system monitors and basic operating systems are included in permanent memory on the computer's *motherboard*. The motherboard usually contains most of the basic circuitry of the computer.

Fig. 1-8. A 5.25-inch floppy disk and a 3.5-inch disk.

A *system monitor* program allows the user to look into memory locations and alter their contents. It is very helpful in diagnosing problems with other problems; however, its use does require some technical knowledge about the architecture of the computer. An *operating system* is an extensive program that tells the computer how to operate. It assigns memory locations for various functions, controls the external storage and retrieval of information, and performs the other control functions needed for the operation of the computer system. A *disk operating system* (DOS) is used to control access to the disk drives. Some examples of current microcomputer disk operating systems in use today are MS-DOS, TRSDOS, CP/M, UNIX, ProDOS, and OS/2.

Once an operating system has been loaded into the computer's memory, it is possible to load and execute *application programs.* Application programs include word processors, spreadsheets, telecommunications, and of course games. While many operating systems and system monitors are written in *machine code* (the most rudimentary programming language, which consists of the actual binary information that is stored in the computer's memory) or assembly language, application programs are written in a variety of languages. Computer languages vary from low level, such as machine and assembly language which deal directly with the computer specifically, to high level, which often have a syntax similar to the English language and thus require much less hardware knowledge. Some examples of high-level languages are Beginners All-purpose Symbolic Instruction Code (BASIC), which is included with nearly all microcomputer systems, Formula Translator (FORTRAN), Pascal, and Common Business Oriented Language (COBOL). The merits of programming in one language or another are beyond the scope of this book.

Modem

The modem is an integral part of any radio-based digital communications system. In digital communications, the modem interfaces between the digital interface and the transceiver. There are many different types and configurations of modems.

A modem inputs bits from a digital device, such as a TNC, and modulates the transmitter with an audio signal (a sine wave) so that the information can be transferred via radio frequency. The modem also can receive modulated signals from the receiver and output bits whose states vary according to the content of the received signal.

Several different modulation (and reciprocally demodulation) methods are in use today. Only the frequency, amplitude, and phase components of a sine wave (Fig. 1-9) can be changed for the transmission of information between modems. The

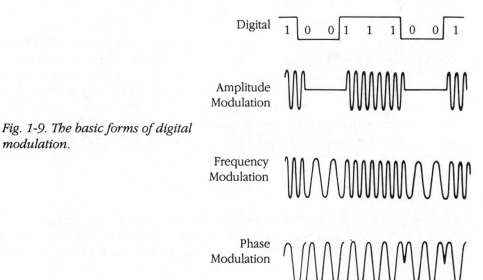

Fig. 1-9. The basic forms of digital modulation.

forms of modulation covered in this chapter are *frequency shift keying* (FSK), *audio frequency shift keying* (AFSK), and *phase shift keying* (PSK). The type of modulation used determines such factors as bandwidth at a given baud rate and the type of transceiver necessary. We'll come back to the subject of modulation after we take a look at baud rate in greater detail.

Baud rates

Earlier, the baud rate was generally defined as the number of bits sent per second. This definition is not entirely accurate in all cases. The baud rate is usually equal to the *bits per second* (BPS), and the two terms are often used incorrectly as synonyms. A baud is a measure of the signaling rate. A baud is actually the number of discrete events per second. For example, a 300-baud signal consists of 300 discrete events per second, and if each event represents a single bit, the BPS equal 300 also. However, in some forms of modulation, each discrete event can represent more than one bit; thus, it is possible to have a rate of 600 or 1,200 BPS from a 300-baud signal.

A *discrete event* is a transition from one level to another in the modulation scheme. For example, changing from a 1,000 Hz signal to a 2,000 Hz signal is a transition (or discrete event). If a demodulator were designed to convert a 1,000 Hz signal into a 1 bit and a 2,000 Hz signal into a 0 bit, we would have a 2-level modulation scheme, and the number of bits each discrete level represents would be 1. If we were to increase the number of frequencies to four (1,000 Hz, 2,000 Hz, 3,000 Hz, and 4,000 Hz) then we could represent 2 bits per event (i.e., 1,000 Hz= 01, 2,000 Hz = 11, 3,000 Hz = 10, and 4,000 Hz = 00).

It is possible to represent the above in the form of a mathematical equation: BPS = BAUD•I. The number of bits sent per second is equal to the baud rate multiplied by the number of bits that each discrete event can represent. Another example: a 1,200-baud signal with each discrete event capable of representing 2 bits has a data transmission rate of 2,400 bits per second.

Channel characteristics

While we're on the subject of equations, this is as good a time as any to introduce two more that are useful when finding the data rate of a communications channel. The first equation is known as Nyquist's equation. It states that the maximum baud rate is equal to twice the bandwidth in Hz (baud=2•bandwidth). For example, a 1,200-baud signal requires 600 Hz bandwidth.

The baud=2•bandwidth equation is actually a simplification of Nyquist's equation. It assumes that each baud represents a single bit. In the case of a baud representing more than 1 bit, Nyquist's full equation is:

$$BPS = 2 \cdot bandwidth \cdot \log_2 (\text{\# of discrete levels}).$$

As you can see, as long as there is only one event per baud (2•1), the log2(2) equals 1, and the equation becomes BPS=2•bandwidth•1. Since the BPS is equal to the baud rate in this case, the equation can be simplified to baud=2•bandwidth as initially introduced.

But, Nyquist's equation assumes a communication channel free of noise, interference, and distortion. Because of this limitation, a communication channel will never obtain the exact characteristics obtained from the equation. It is useful as an approximation and gives an actual value for analysis, even if it is very optimistic.

The next equation, Shannon's law, is somewhat more useful, since it takes noise and interference into account. The amount of random and thermal noise on a channel is measured by the signal power to noise power ratio, more commonly called the signal-to-noise ratio. The signal-to-noise ratio is usually represented as S/N. The signal-to-noise ratio is included in Shannon's equation as follows:

$$BPS = bandwidth \bullet log2(1+S/N)$$

More on modulation

As mentioned earlier, a sine wave can be characterized by frequency, amplitude, and phase. Phase is useful as a signaling device only if the frequency remains constant. Since a sine wave completes a full cycle in 360 degrees, the amount of lag that one signal has compared to another can be used to indicate a transition or discrete event.

The difference between FSK and AFSK frequency modulation has to do with the method used to transmit the generated signal. FSK is classified as direct modulation, and AFSK as indirect modulation. In direct modulation, the transmitter carrier frequency is shifted up and down to transmit the analog signal. In indirect modulation, the transmitter's carrier remains stable while an external signal is superimposed upon the carrier. It is the external signal that varies, not the transmitter's carrier.

AFSK is usually easier to implement with modern transceivers because all signal generation can be done externally of the transmitter. The audio signal can be simply fed into the transceiver's mic input. Since most transceivers do not include direct FSK ports, some modification is usually necessary to implement FSK directly. Regardless of whether the transmitter is AFSK- or FSK-controlled, the transmitted signal is the same.

In (A) FSK, the frequency of the sine wave is varied to indicate transmission of a binary 1 or 0. As mentioned before, the bandwidth required varies according to the signaling rate, so the minimum difference or shift between the 2 frequencies is dependent upon the signaling rate. If a signaling rate of 200 baud is used, the frequency pairs used to represent the binary 0 and 1 might be 1,000 Hz and 1,200 Hz, respectively.

Although it is possible to have a multilevel modulation scheme using FSK, it is not normally utilized. At present, AFSK is the means of digital modulation most used in amateur radio communications, packet included. However, that may soon change as we look for methods that allow us to transmit more information through less bandwidth and under poorer channel conditions.

Phase shift keying offers the benefits listed previously and may see increased use in the future in packet radio. PSK transmits information by changing the phase of the signal. If the phase is shifted between 0 degrees and 180 degrees, it is possible to transmit information with each phase degree representing a binary character. If more phase shifts were added, 90 degrees and 270 degrees, 2 binary characters could be represented in each phase shift. For example, 0 degrees = 10, 90 degrees = 01, 180 degrees = 11, and 270 degrees = 00. Each pair of binary characters is called a *dibit*. Using the dibit, the BPS has been doubled while maintaining the baud rate.

It is easy to see why PSK could be one of the modulation schemes to be reckoned with in the future. If more phase shifts were added and some amplitude modulation were thrown in, the data rate could conceivably be quadrupled. *Quaternary amplitude modulation (QAM)* is such a form, in which PSK is combined with amplitude modulation to encode 4 bits per transition. The one drawback to PSK is that it requires more complicated modem units than regular FSK.

Conclusion

This chapter has taken a broad look at many issues relating to digital communications. Aside from the introduction to the various modes of amateur radio digital communications, you should have a fair understanding of how information is converted to digital form and transmitted over a radio channel.

Don't be too concerned if you had some difficulty understanding the more technical material included in this chapter. You will find it easier to understand many of the later chapters now that you have seen this information. After you've been through the book once, come back to this chapter and reread the parts you found confusing. I'm certain it will all fall together for you then.

2

The history of
amateur digital
communications

THE HISTORY OF AMATEUR RADIO DIGITAL COMMUNICATIONS IS VERY INTERESTING, and for the newcomer to digital communications, knowledge of its history will help explain the evolution of digital communication technologies, the reason certain operating practices occur, and the root of some of the terminology. Some terms are used in this chapter that have not yet been introduced; they are explained in later chapters, and a brief explanation of most terms can be found in the glossary. So without further discussion, I'll start at the beginning.

Radiotelegraphy

The most basic digital mode in use in amateur radio is also the first mode ever used in amateur radio. *Radiotelegraphy*, more commonly known as CW (Continuous Wave) or somewhat imprecisely as Morse code, is simply the sending of telegraph signals over radio. The first telegraph signals were sent in the early 1800s.

The first telegraph systems were very simple. A switch or key was used to regulate the flow of current through an electrical circuit. This electrical circuit took the form of a wire running from the sending location to the receiving station, and often the earth served as the common ground.

The early telegraph systems used a magnetic needle (basically a simple compass) to detect the presence of current in the circuit. First discovered by Hans Orested, a magnetic needle will pivot when exposed to the magnetic field generated by the flow of current through a conductor. The first successful implementation of the "deflecting needle telegraph" was the 1837 introduction of the railway telegraph in England.

Samuel Morse developed the next advance in telegraphy, the electromagnetic decoder. The electromagnet was first discovered in the 1820s, and Morse learned of electromagnetic theory from the work of Michael Faraday and Joseph Henry in the early 1830s. In Morse's first system, a pencil was attached to an iron armature that was pulled to the electromagnet when current was flowing through the telegraph line. A strip of paper was kept moving beneath the pencil, and the movements of the armature were recorded.

Morse soon developed a code to represent alphanumeric symbols. Morse's code was based on two elements, a dot and a dash. The dot is a signal of short duration, and the dash is three times as long as the dot. By combining the two elements, Morse was able to represent the alphabet, numbers, and punctuation.

Morse, along with Alfred Vail, soon improved upon the original electromagnetic decoder. The new device marked only the dot and dash elements as lines on the strip of paper. Morse's improved electromagnetic decoder was used for the historical 1844 demonstration during which he sent "What hath God wrought" from Baltimore to Washington, D.C. However, soon the paper strip was abandoned; as telegraph operators gained more experience, they were able to copy the code by listening to the armature clacking against the electromagnet.

Copying by ear soon gained more acceptance when a relay was attached to the telegraph line in place of the standard electromagnet. The relay was used to switch a buzzer powered by local power at the receiver. In addition to making copying by ear easier, the relay would work with lower power signals, allowing the length of telegraph lines between stations to be increased.

Historically, the first use of radiotelegraphy is credited to Marconi in 1897. It is at this point that most amateur radio operators will recognize the beginnings of our hobby. The invention of the vacuum tube in 1907 by Lee De Forest did much to improve the electronic technology of the day and greatly increased the capabilities of both radio and wire-based telegraph systems.

Radiotelegraphy's fundamentals have not changed much over the intervening years. Today we have electronic keyers of all types, and it is possible to operate CW without even knowing the Morse code. However, to many amateurs the joy of operating CW with a straight key is as prevalent today as it was during the formative days of amateur radio.

Radioteletype

The development of radioteletype occurred in the same time frame as radiotelegraphy. It was in 1874 that Emile Baudot completed development of a new method of transmitting information. Although his method used the same medium as Morse's telegraph, Baudot's system utilized a different coding system. Morse code is an uneven code made up of 3 states: dot, dash, and null (or no) signal. The Baudot code is an even code made up of 2 states: signal and no signal.

In an uneven code, the length of the code representing the symbols being sent is not constant for all symbols (i.e., the code of the letter E—a dot—is shorter than that for the letter J—dot dash dash dash). In the Baudot code, all the symbols are represented by 5 units, or elements. Since only 2 conditions are possible, the binary system can be used to represent the condition of each element.

Thus, the Baudot code can be represented as a string of 5 bits (i.e., 10101). These bits, or elements, are sent in order at a prescribed speed. The primary advantage of the Baudot code is that more automated systems could be developed.

The original Baudot systems used a keyboard with 5 keys. Each character's code was entered by pressing the appropriate keys. Usually, the code was punched into a paper strip. When the message was complete, the tape was run through a sending machine at a constant speed.

It's not too difficult to foresee the development of the teleprinter from this stage. The Baudot code made automated receiving easy, since the length of each character was the same. An alphanumeric keyboard that automatically generated the appropriate code for each key pressed was also a natural progression.

These teleprinters quickly gained in popularity, and soon there was a large network of interconnected teleprinters. The Telex network evolved out of this growth. Baudot teleprinters were the primary system of data communication in the world until the development of solid state terminals in the 1970s. Even today, mechanical teleprinters continue to be used in many parts of the world.

Radio amateurs did not use radioteletype to any great extent until the end of World War II. However, after that time, using surplus military and commercial teleprinters, amateurs in increasing numbers experimented with Baudot RTTY.

Amateur RTTY systems remained pretty much the same until the microcomputer revolution in the mid-1970s. RTTY's growth was limited by the nature of the mechanical teleprinters that were necessary to operate the mode. Mechanical teleprinters were noisy, often greasy and oily, and required mechanical adeptness to keep in working order. The solid-state terminals quickly changed all that.

RTTY went from being one of the most mechanical and noisiest modes to one of the most electronic and quiet modes. This transformation, along with the advent of ASCII RTTY, did much to spur interest in RTTY among amateurs. ASCII RTTY was a direct result of the increasing use of microcomputer technology in the ham shack.

The ASCII code is a 7-level code, similar to the Baudot code in concept, that is commonly used by microcomputers to represent alphanumeric and control characters. In order to use an ASCII-based microcomputer or terminal for Baudot RTTY, the 7-element ASCII code for each character has to be converted to its equivalent in the 5-level Baudot code. At the receiving end, the Baudot code has to be converted back to ASCII for display on solid-state microcomputer terminals.

Based on this expanding base of ASCII machines, the FCC authorized the transmission of the ASCII code on March 17, 1980. This date marks the beginning of an important era in amateur radio history: the era of modern amateur radio digital communications. Today we all benefit from the systems and technologies developed over the past decade. This leads us nicely into the next major digital communications mode in amateur radio: packet radio.

Packet radio

The first studies of packet networking were conducted by the Rand Corporation in 1964. The term *packet* was introduced by D.W. Davies of the British National Physics

Laboratory in 1965. Work started on developing an actual packet network for the United States Advanced Research Projects Agency (DARPA) in 1969.

The DARPA network, named ARPANET, was set up by Bolt, Beranek, and Newman, Inc., and included packet switching. Other packet-switching networks were developed around the world by both private enterprises and governments.

The first packet networks were all cable-based (i.e., all transmission was over cables). The first large-scale packet radio experiments, where transmission was over radio frequencies, began in 1970. One of the largest and most significant packet radio networks was ALOHANET, based at the University of Hawaii.

ALOHANET linked a number of computers and users together using packet-switching technology over radio links (Fig. 2-1). ALOHANET had access to ARPANET and satellite relays and was established to investigate the mathematical and practical aspects of a random-access packet system. Many of the techniques used in amateur packet radio systems were first developed as a result of ALOHANET.

ALOHANET operated on two frequencies: 407.350 MHz and 413.475 MHz. The first was used to transmit from user terminals to the central computer (called the *menehune*), and the second was used by the menehune for transmissions back to the user terminals. Repeaters were included for terminals located too far from the menehune for direct communications.

Each radio station was called a *node*. The equipment at each node consisted of a standard commercial VHF radio, a 9,600-baud modem, and either a Terminal Control Unit (TCU) or a Programmable Control Unit (PCU) for nodes with more than one user terminal attached to it. The TCU and PCU are the equivalent of today's TNCs.

Many different protocols and contention schemes were experimented with on ALOHANET. For more information on ALOHANET, see the following references:

- *Packet Radio* by Robert Roleau VE2PY and Ian Hodgson VE2BEN from TAB Books.
- *Computer Networks* by Andrew S. Tanenbaum from Prentice-Hall.

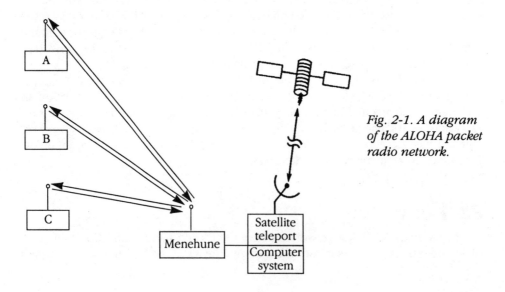

Fig. 2-1. A diagram of the ALOHA packet radio network.

Amateur packet radio

Amateur packet radio has an interesting history. The following sections describe the development of packet radio over the years.

Canada: The initial sparks

Amateur packet radio operation got its start in Canada in April 1978, when the Department of Communications (DOC) announced that it intended to change the regulations to allow packet operation on 220 MHz. Several Canadian amateurs immediately began investigating packet radio operation and were soon busy developing the necessary equipment for packet operation. The first amateur packet radio transmissions occurred on May 31, 1978, in Canada.

The first amateur packets were sent using a packet radio system developed by the Montreal Amateur Radio Club. Their network was named MP-Net and was the first amateur packet radio system in the world. The Montreal group was using a complete homebrew system with a CSMA/CD protocol. The transmission speeds were both 1,200- and 2,400-baud AFSK on the 220 MHz band.

A description of the MP-Net is given by two of the participants, Roleau VE2PY and Hodgson VE2BEN, in their book, *Packet Radio*. The authors each published an article on the MP-Net system. The first, titled "The Packet Radio Revolution," was written by Roleau and appeared in the December 1978 issue of *73 Magazine*. Hodgson's article, "An Introduction to Packet Radio," was published in the June 1979 issue of the now-defunct *Ham Radio Magazine*.

The next Canadian group to get a packet system up and running was the Vancouver Amateur Digital Communication Group (VADCG), founded by Doug Lockhart in January 1979. The VADCG system is the best known of the Canadian systems because of its work in spreading packet radio to the United States.

The first hardware device dedicated to handling packet radio communications was developed by the VADCG (Fig. 2-2). This device was given the name *terminal node controller*, which has stuck to the present day. An amateur packet radio protocol that gained a wide following in the early days of packet radio was also developed by the group.

The Vancouver system was configured as several users with terminals and TNCs communicating with a central device called a *station node controller* (SNC) at 1,200 baud on 144 MHz. When individual users first connected to the SNC, they were assigned a numeric address. This address was included in all transmissions to that user's station. All communications between users took place through the SNC.

The VADCG sold their TNCs to amateurs in other countries (although packet radio was not yet legal for United States amateurs). They published the first amateur packet radio newsletter, "The Packet". The VADCG also transmitted packet beacon messages on 14.0765 MHz so others outside of Canada where packet operation was not legal could check the operation of their TNCs.

The third Canadian group to get a packet system operational was based in Ottawa. The Ottawa group began operation in 1980, and its system consisted of a

Fig. 2-2. A partially assembled original VADCG TNC.

polling protocol and SNC. Transmissions were at 9,600 baud using FSK modulation techniques.

United States: The flames take hold

Amateur packet radio operation was not legal for United States amateurs for about eighteen months after it was legalized in Canada. Finally, on March 17, 1980, the Federal Communications Commission authorized ASCII transmissions in response to the wide proliferation of ASCII-based computer systems. The first amateur packet radio system run by United States amateurs was put up near San Francisco, California, and was activated on December 10, 1980. This digipeater was developed by Hank Magnuski KA6M and consisted of a homebrew TNC using a modified version of the VADCG's protocol.

On the East Coast, the Amateur Radio Research and Development Corporation (AMRAD) began publishing information on packet radio in its newsletter. The first amateur packet radio station on the East Coast was activated by Bill Moran W4MIB on May 4, 1981. The East Coast system also used a modified VADCG system.

Packet remained in the experimenter's workshop, out of the amateur radio public's eye, until the October 1981 issue of *QST Magazine* was published by the Amateur Radio Relay League. This issue of *QST* contained an interesting article on packet radio, "The Making of An Amateur Packet-Radio Network," written by David W. Borden K8MMO and Paul L. Rinaldo W4RI. The article announced what was to be the first of many ARRL Amateur Radio Computer Networking Conferences on October 16, 1981. This article had a significant impact on amateur packet radio by introducing packet to the general amateur population.

The first ARRL Computer Networking Conference was held in Gaithersburg, Maryland. It was designed to serve as a general meeting of North American amateurs who were interested in developing packet radio. One of the attendees, Den Connors KD2S, would later do much toward that goal.

Tucson: Fire in the desert

After attending the networking conference, Den Connors returned to Tucson, Arizona, and on October 29, 1981, gave a talk at the Tucson chapter of the IEEE computer society. His talk was centered on amateur packet radio; specifically, developing a packet system based on the 6809 microprocessor. Several people in attendance were interested in Connor's speech and decided to meet at a later date to discuss amateur packet radio activity in Tucson.

The meeting was held on November 6, 1981, and six people were in attendance: Lyle Johnson WA7GXD, Mark Baker, Dave McClain N7AIG, Marc Chamberlain WA7PXW, Jerry Clark K7KZ, and Den Connors KD2S. The result of this meeting was the formation of the Tucson Amateur Packet Radio Corporation (TAPR) and a commitment to develop a complete TNC with on-board modem and power supply.

At the time of the first TAPR meeting, the cost involved in equipping an amateur packet radio station was around $300 for the VADCG TNC PC board, parts, a modem, and a power supply. TAPR hoped to be able to develop a TNC with all the necessary components and accessories at half this cost. With this goal in mind, they set off on the development of what would be known as the Alpha TNC.

The Alpha TNC was produced several months later and was based on the 6502 microprocessor. Only 12 Alpha boards were made and distributed to selected participants for testing in April 1982. The Alpha board served as a trial run for TAPR, helping them to learn more about the details involved in producing and distributing TNCs.

On June 9, 1982, the first packets were transmitted by an Alpha TNC. Later, on June 18, an Alpha TNC successfully received transmitted packets. With the knowledge gained from the testing of the Alpha TNC, TAPR began to prepare an updated TNC design for the next stage in its TNC development program, the Beta TNC.

The spreading fire

By this time, many amateurs in the United States had begun developing packet radio systems. Several other packet groups had sprung up around the country. Many systems were using the modified VADCG protocol first introduced in California. The TAPR Alpha TNC was using a prototype testing protocol. AMRAD and RATS had developed a protocol based on the CCITT X.25 protocol, which they called AX.25. By mid-1982, there was some concern about compatibility between systems, and with the upcoming launch of OSCAR 10 and the prospect of wide-area packet communications between the different systems, amateurs wanted to establish a nationwide standard protocol.

In October 1982, the president of AMSAT, Tom Clark W3IWI, called a meeting of United States packet groups with the intention of agreeing on a standard protocol. The three contenders for the standard protocol were VADCG, TAPR/DA, and AX.25. The outcome of the meeting was a new version of AX.25 that supported digipeaters. Thus, AX.25 became the standard protocol for amateur packet operation in the United States.

Tucson: Still burning

Back in Tucson, work was continuing on the Beta TNC, now to utilize the new AX.25 protocol. The Beta TNC was to be distributed to a much larger number of users for testing. About 170 Beta TNCs were eventually distributed. By December 1982, the Beta TNC was nearing completion. The first few boards had been assembled and were operating properly, and the printed circuit boards and components were delivered. The protocol and other software development was being handled by Harold Price NK6K, Dave Henderson KD4NL, and Margaret Morrison KV7D. At the end of 1982, approximately 200 TNCs were in existence in North America.

The finished Beta TNC consisted of a 6809 microprocessor, a hardware HDLC system, 24K of ROM, 6K of RAM, and LED status indicators all on an 8-x-8-inch PC board. The Beta TNCs were sent to numerous sites for testing. In the middle of all the Beta TNC activity, TAPR held its first annual meeting on February 5, 1983. The software underwent many modifications and revisions, and the comments of all Beta TNC testers were noted.

The second ARRL Computer Networking Conference was held in March 1983 in San Francisco.

The July 1983 issue of *Ham Radio Magazine* featured the Beta TNC on the cover and included the first of a two-part article on packet radio title "Amateur Packet Radio: Part I" by Margaret Morrison KV7D and Dan Morrison KV7B. The August issue contains the second part of the article, which covers the technical aspects of the Beta TNC.

The fire grows larger

Now that the Beta TNC test period was coming to an end, TAPR was gearing up for full-scale production of TNC kits for distribution to the mass amateur radio market. Prototype TNC boards were constructed in August 1983 and preparation made for general distribution. On November 21, 1983, the first shipment of 100 TNCs was ready.

The TAPR TNC was supplied in kit form. The kit and assembly manual received rave reviews from the amateur community. The PC board was of excellent quality and the manual was very informative, with an easy-to-follow assembly section. All in all, over 2,500 TAPR TNC kits were sold by TAPR.

Also in August 1983, another TNC, called the PK-1, was introduced by GLB Electronics. The GLB TNC initially only supported the VADCG protocol; however, AX.25 was added quickly. In the GLB TNC, the HDLC system was handled using software rather than hardware, as in the TAPR TNCs. This resulted in a strange situation: a user could not type on the terminal and receive frames over the radio at the same time. By the end of 1983, approximately 650 TNCs existed in North America.

In February 1984, the first W0RLI packet bulletin board system (BBS) was put on the air by Hank Oredson W0RLI. This system has become the standard packet BBS in the United States.

The third ARRL Computer Networking Conference was held in April 1984 in Trenton, New Jersey. The Dayton Hamvention was held two weeks later and attracted over 300 attendees. At the 1984 Dayton Hamvention, TAPR's president, Lyle Johnson, was presented with the first Technical Achievement Award for his work on the TAPR TNC. Later that year, Doug Lockhart received the CRRL Certificate of Merit in recognition of his pioneering work in amateur packet radio. Today, Doug Lockhart is widely recognized as "the father of amateur packet radio."

Another significant event occurred at the 1984 Dayton Hamvention: AEA introduced the first TAPR TNC clone (Fig. 2-3). TAPR had made arrangements to sell the rights to its TNC design for a flat fee of $500. This step was taken to encourage commercial manufacturers to get involved with packet radio. The AEA PKT-1 is identical to the TAPR TNC in most respects.

AEA began to run a series of full-page ads in major amateur publications for its TNC. By the end of 1984, the number of TNCs in existence in North America had grown to approximately 2,500.

On March 25, 1985, the FCC eliminated the requirement that a description of all special digital codes used above 50 MHz be included in the station log. The fourth ARRL Computer Networking Conference was held on March 30, 1985, in San Francisco.

In March 1985, Heathkit introduced its TAPR TNC clone. The initial production run of 500 units in April sold out in 3 weeks. At the 1985 Dayton Hamvention, Kantronics introduced its TNC, the Packet Communicator. In late April, TAPR announced that it was stopping production of its TNC.

TAPR felt that the commercial TNC clones were being produced faster and at a lower cost than TAPR could accomplish. TAPR decided to sell its remaining stock of TNCs at discount prices and clear the way for more developmental work. TAPR's next step was the TNC-2.

The TAPR TNC-2 was a new TNC design based on the Z-80 microprocessor. It contained many new features, such as lower power consumption and smaller size than the original TAPR TNC (now called the TNC-1). The TNC-2 development went rather smoothly, and test versions were distributed in May 1985.

The July and August 1985 issues of *QST Magazine* each contain an article on packet radio written by Harold Price. The August issue featured a TAPR TNC-2 on the cover (Fig. 2-4).

In July 1985, TAPR announced it would begin accepting orders by telephone for the TAPR TNC-2 kit beginning at 9:00 A.M. on Monday, August 19, 1985. Only 300 TNCs were available, and only one kit was allowed per customer—first come, first served.

On Monday morning, the telephones at TAPR headquarters began to ring, and they did not stop. Orders for the TNC-2 were coming in at a phenomenal rate.

Fig. 2-3. The AEA PKT-1.

Fig. 2-4. Packet radio newsletters and cover articles that have been published over the past several years.

Around noon, TAPR received a call from one of the telephone company engineers, telling them that the level of incoming calls had completely saturated the phone system. The phone systems shut down three different times that day. At times, other Tucson telephone users could not even get a dial tone. Needless to say, TAPR quickly sold its supply of TNCs and took advance orders for another 350 units over a period of two days.

TAPR also sold the rights to the TNC-2. However, this time the cost was $5,000 plus a royalty. TAPR felt the risk involved in a commercial company producing packet radio equipment had come down enough that the companies would be willing to put up more money. Soon many versions of the TNC-2 were being sold by a variety of commercial companies (Fig. 2-5).

The fifth ARRL Computer Networking Conference was held on March 9, 1986, in Orlando, Florida. At the 1987 Dayton Hamvention, Hank Oredson was presented with that year's Technical Excellence Award for his development of the W0RLI packet bulletin board system. During 1987, packet radio really began to grow. At the end of 1987, well over 20,000 TNCs were estimated to be in existence. By the summer of 1988, that number had grown to over 35,000.

Fig. 2-5. The Pac-Comm TNC-200 circuit board.

It is safe to predict that packet radio will continue to grow during the 1990s. At the beginning of the new decade, the number of TNCs had grown to well over 60,000, although the number of units does not directly correspond to the number of users, since many users own more than one TNC. Packet radio has developed rapidly over the past decade and much more lies ahead.

AMTOR

The latest mode of digital communications in amateur radio proves the truth in the adage "everything old is new again." AMTOR, which stands for Amateur Teleprinting Over Radio, is a very capable mode based on the original Baudot code. However, AMTOR does much to improve the performance of traditional Baudot RTTY.

AMTOR evolved from a commercial teleprinter system used for maritime communications. This maritime system is known as SITOR (simplex telex over radio) and TOR (teleprinting on radio). Largely through the efforts of Peter Martinez G3PLX, SITOR was modified to meet amateur radio's needs and requirements. The result was AMTOR. Through articles in Britain's *Radio Communication* magazine, as well as *QST*, Martinez promoted AMTOR to the amateur radio community.

AMTOR, like packet, is an error-correcting mode of digital communication. Because of the extreme noise and fading often experienced on the HF bands, where most all RTTY is operated, most RTTY QSOs invariably have a few disruptions, resulting in some lost or scrambled characters. AMTOR solves this problem by automatically requesting the retransmission of data that was not received correctly.

AMTOR is able to do so by modifying the Baudot code to include two extra elements, bringing the total number of elements per character to seven. These 7 elements are always in a precise ratio of 4:3; each character has four 1 elements and three 0 elements. By checking for the proper ratio, the AMTOR receiving station can ensure correct reception.

On January 27, 1983, the FCC authorized AMTOR usage in the amateur radio service. Since that time, AMTOR has enjoyed rapid acceptance among digital operators. AMTOR is still gaining acceptance among newer digital operators and will continue to grow steadily throughout the 1990s.

Conclusion

This chapter has examined the history of the major digital modes in amateur radio. The following several chapters cover each mode individually in great detail. Hopefully, this chapter has given you an appreciation of the development and evolution of the digital modes in use today. With a modern multimode interface, you can operate all of these modes, so you don't need to confine yourself to one or two modes. Indeed, a great deal of the recent growth experienced in amateur radio digital communications can be attributed to amateurs wanting to utilize fully the capabilities of their multimode interfaces.

Undoubtedly many other important events, individuals, and groups that have contributed greatly to the present state of amateur radio digital communications are not mentioned in this chapter. I apologize to those I missed.

3

Radiotelegraphy

NOT MANY DEVELOPMENTS OF THE 1800S REMAIN TODAY AS CLOSE TO THEIR original form as does radiotelegraphy by Morse code. Radiotelegraphy using Morse code is one of the fundamental—digital or otherwise—modes in use in amateur radio. From the beginnings of amateur radio around the turn of the century to today, amateur radio operators have been operating radiotelegraphy using the Morse code.

Most amateurs refer to radiotelegraphy with the more familiar term CW, for Continuous Wave, or more simply as Morse code. CW describes the means by which the transmitter transmits the signal. (I'll examine this method in more detail later in this chapter.)

Morse code is the standard code used by amateur radio operators the world over to communicate using CW. Of course, no technical obstacle prevents using another code. However, the Morse code has stood the test of time and serves as a special language that bonds all CW operators together.

Morse code

There are several forms of Morse code: Early Morse code, American Morse code, and International Morse code. Today, International Morse code is used by amateur radio operators and is the specific code referenced when the generic term "Morse code" is used. A Morse code chart containing the most popular characters is included in appendix A.

Technically, Morse code is an uneven digital code. In an uneven code, the number of characters that make up each character are not equal; thus, some characters have more elements than others. There are two signaling elements in the Morse code: a short cadence, known as a *dot*, and a longer cadence, called a *dash*. When

27

speaking the Morse code, the dot element is pronounced "dit" and the dash element is pronounced "dah."

Morse code can be sent at various speeds, much as a person can speak slowly or more quickly. The speed at which Morse code is being sent is measured in words per minute (WPM). In order to understand how this works, a knowledge of the fundamental timing characteristics of the elements is necessary.

The most fundamental timing element in Morse code is the dot. A dash is three times as long as a dot. Thus, if it takes one-third of a second to send a dot, a dash sent at the same speed will take one second to send. The dot and dash elements making up a single character are separated by a space equal to one dot, and the space between individual characters is three dots (or one dash). The space between words is seven dots. These spaces, or pauses, let the receiving station know when the end of a character or word occurs. Figure 3-1 shows this relationship graphically.

If each character in Morse code were composed of the same number of elements, the spaces between characters would not be as important. For example, the Morse code for the letter E is one dot (•), the letter A is one dot followed by one dash (•—), and the letter U is two dots followed by one dash (••—). By now you should recognize the problem that can occur when the characters are not spaced properly.

$$T_2 = T_1 \times 3$$

Fig. 3-1. The basic unit of Morse code is the dot. The dash is three times as long as the dot.

If you were trying to send the characters E and A using Morse code (perhaps as part of the word EAT), you would send one dot, pause for the time it would take to send three more dots, then send one dot, pause for the time it would take to send one dot, and finally send a dash. At the receiving end, the operator would receive a dot, and then hearing the pause and thus knowing the complete character had been sent, would write down the letter E. The receiver would then hear another dot, quickly followed by a dash, and another pause, and then write down an A. If the sender were to forget to include the pause between the E and the A, the receiver would hear two dots followed by a dash, and would write down the letter U. (As an interesting aside, the most common character in the English language, E, is also the shortest in Morse code, one dot. The remainder of the alphabet is ordered by frequency, with the more common characters having the shorter Morse code equivalents.)

As you have seen, timing is very important when using Morse code. When a dot is sent quickly, the dash is shorter, and the pauses are also shorter. When a dot is sent slowly, the dash is longer, as are the pauses. Maintaining a constant timing relationship when sending Morse code characters at various speeds is one of the hardest parts of sending Morse code manually using a straight key. (I'll examine the various systems used to signal Morse code over radio a little later.)

Calculating the speed at which Morse code is being sent is not an exact science. Since the speed is measured in words per minute, the definition of a word must first be established. In the past, someone found that the average word in the English language is five characters long. The word "Paris" is a standard word chosen for calculating sending speed.

If you wish to send Morse code at 5 WPM, adjust your sending speed so that you can send "Paris" five times in one minute. (Figure 3-2 gives a graphical look at the timing characteristics of the word "Paris" in Morse code.) A quick trick that some operators use to estimate their sending speed is to count the number of dashes they send in five seconds; the number is roughly equal to the sending speed in WPM.

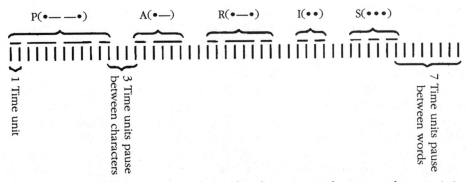

Fig. 3-2. The word Paris *is commonly used to demonstrate the timing characteristics of Morse code. The pause between characters is the equivalent of three dots (one dash), and the pause between words is the length of seven dots.*

Many Morse code operators, as well as some training audiocassettes, find it easier to send Morse code elements making up individual characters much faster than the desired sending speed. The spaces between characters and words are then lengthened correspondingly to compensate. They do this based on the assumption that it is easier to learn to copy Morse code at faster speeds if the beginner starts out hearing the characters sent faster.

Equipment

CW is one of the easiest modes to operate as far as equipment is concerned. Even the most basic transmitters and transceivers are capable of operating CW. Most any shortwave receiver can be used to copy CW, provided the receiver has a beat frequency oscillator (BFO).

When CW is transmitted, a switch of some sort is used to "key" the transmission of a constant carrier. By opening and closing the switch, the operator can send Morse code characters. At the receiving end, a receiver, with its BFO active, tuned to the correct frequency will receive the CW signal. The BFO produces an audible tone that is sent to the receiver's speaker whenever the transmitted carrier signal is received. Thus, the receiver emits tone when the operator of the transmitter has the "key" switch closed.

As the transmitting operator opens and closes the key switch, more commonly called a *keyer*, to form Morse code characters, the person at the receiving end can hear the corresponding tones. (Some transceivers feature a QSK mode, in which the receiver turns on when the keyer is released. This feature allows others to break in easily, interrupting the sender if need be, without having to wait for the sender to finish his entire message.)

Keyers come in a wide variety of forms. The most basic is the straight key, a simple lever-like device. One end of the lever is attached to a spring so that the switch is normally open. To send, the operator pushes down on the other end of the lever, causing it to pivot on its mount and stretch the spring. When the operator has pushed down far enough, the contact will close, and the transmitter will "key-up." To stop transmitting, the operator lets up on the lever, and the spring pulls the back end of the lever down, breaking the contact. By controlling these actions, the operator is able to send Morse code characters.

A wide variety of more automatic keyers, called bugs, are available. Bugs are usually easier to use than straight keys. A bug can be mechanical or electronic. Typically, a bug will have two paddles (or one that moves in two directions). Pressing one paddle causes the keyer to send a dot, and pressing the other paddle causes the keyer to send a dash. Electronic bugs have a speed adjustment, so the sending speed can be set by turning a knob.

Computers also can be used to send CW. Once the speed is set, characters are sent by typing on the keyboard. All the timing and spacing is done automatically by the computer. Computers can even be used to receive Morse code.

In the late 1970s and early 1980s, several stand-alone Morse code keyboards and separate Morse code receivers were on the market. The receivers had a 10 or so character display and would automatically decode Morse code. These units became obsolete with the introduction of multimode digital interface units. The latest multimode units can send and receive Morse code easily. Characters sent and received are displayed on the terminal's display.

Operating CW

Almost every amateur is reasonably proficient at CW operating procedures. Nevertheless, for the purposes of completeness and review, as well as an introduction for newcomers, I'll cover some of the operating basics in this section. CW is a very enjoyable mode to operate and provides a link with amateur radio's beginnings that we can all experience today.

The world of CW operation is full of abbreviations. Not surprisingly, the abbreviations are used to make life easier for CW operators; however, it can have the opposite effect on newcomers. The easiest way to get used to the strange language of CW is to monitor CW communications, known as QSOs, for a while.

Most CW QSOs start out with a CQ, which stands for "calling all amateurs." The CQ can be more specific, such as CQ DX for "calling all foreign amateurs" or CQ GA for "calling all Georgia amateurs." When sending a CQ, you are soliciting a contact.

The CQ is followed by the characters *DE*, meaning "this is," and your callsign. Send CQ a few times, then send a *K* to indicate you are standing by for responses. A useful abbreviation to know at this point is *QRS*, which means "slow down," for use in case a responding station is sending too quickly for you to copy.

Continue the QSO by sending the other station's callsign followed by DE and your callsign. When you are done for the time being, send the callsigns over again followed by an $\overline{AR}$ and a K. ($\overline{AR}$, with a bar on top, is sent by sending an A and then an R without any pause between the characters. It means "end of message)." When you are done talking and have said 73 (disconnect request), end your last transmission by sending the callsigns followed by $\overline{SK}$, meaning "end of QSO."

Conclusion

Morse code is as old as amateur radio itself. Learning, or relearning, Morse code can seem difficult. Many systems are available for learning the code, but the surest way is regular practice, either by monitoring on-air QSOs or by listening to code on practice audio tapes. The effort is well worth it.

Many of us become enamored with our multimode interfaces, easily sending and receiving Morse code electronically. I'd like to encourage you to turn off the black box every now and then to operate CW with a straight key (well, a bug's okay too) and copy by ear. After all, Morse code is the only digital code that can be copied by ear without the aid of decoding equipment.

4

Radioteletype

UNTIL THE EARLY 1980S, WHEN MOST AMATEURS TALKED ABOUT DIGITAL COMMUNICATIONS, they were referring to radioteletype. The development and expansion of amateur radioteletype began shortly after the end of World War II and continues to the present time. The end of the war was accompanied by the spread of wired and wireless Teletype networks, as well as a surplus of teleprinter devices that made their way into the amateur radio service. Mechanical teleprinters, more commonly known as Teletypes, were the mainstay of amateur radioteletype operations until the late 1970s.

Today, mechanical teleprinter machines are rarely found in common usage. The advent of solid-state computer terminals ushered in a new era in amateur digital communications. Radioteletype (RTTY), once one of the most mechanical and noisy modes, quickly became one of the most electronic and quiet. However, the world of RTTY is still full of terminology that dates back to the days of teleprinters, so in order to fully understand RTTY today, a brief look into the past is necessary.

The teleprinter era

In chapter 2, the initial development of RTTY was discussed. To review, efforts to increase the automation and efficiency of Morse code telegraphy led to the development of a new system of telegraphy by Emile Baudot that has evolved into the RTTY of today. Baudot's system used an even code, in which every character was represented by a series of five elements.

Teleprinters are mechanical devices that are designed to code and decode this five-element code. Physically, a teleprinter looks much like an electronic typewriter. A keyboard is used to type in the characters in the order they are to be transmitted. The characters are converted by a mechanical system inside the teleprinter into their

Baudot code equivalent. This code is directly transmitted or stored on a paper tape, or both.

Paper tape was the most common medium for storage of digital data (along with punch cards) until the development of magnetic recording systems. The paper tape, about 1 inch wide and stored on rolls or fan-folded, was punched in a device known as a *perforator* or more commonly, as a *tape punch*. The codes for individual characters are stored across the width of the tape. These tapes could then be saved for automated transmission at a later time using a tape reader.

Although the paper punch and reader often were incorporated in the same housing as the teleprinter, in some cases they were not. In addition to the tape devices, other devices such as the radio interface unit (known as a TU for terminal unit) had to be linked together, much as TNCs and printers must be interfaced to a personal computer today. The RS-232 and Centronics interfaces of the teleprinter era was the *current loop*.

Electromagnets are used in teleprinters and related devices to detect the presence of mark and space signals. These electromagnets are triggered by the presence of an electrical current. Thus, by wiring all of the devices together in a loop, one device could turn the current flow on and off as needed to transfer the Baudot codes to other devices connected to the loop, also called the *local loop*.

To give an example of how this worked, imagine an incoming RTTY signal is received by the TU. As the received tones shift from mark to space and back in accordance with the Baudot code, the TU transfers this digital information to the other devices by triggering the flow of current in the local loop in accordance with the received signal. The teleprinter's electromagnets are triggered by the flow of current through the loop, and through the teleprinter's mechanical systems, type the appropriate alphanumeric symbols on paper. At the same time, the tape punch stores the received code on paper tape, its mechanisms also controlled by the flow of current in the local loop.

The electrical characteristics of the local loop have varied over time. Early loops used a current of 60 mA at between 100 and 300 Vdc to trigger the electromagnets. With more modern teleprinters, the loop current was reduced to 20 mA. In the early days of the solid-state revolution, many computer hobbyists used teleprinters to interface with the early personal computers, such as the Altair and IMSAI, by converting the current loop to a low-voltage digital signal. Using such adaptors, it is possible to interface a current loop teleprinter with an RS-232 or TTL interface.

There are several types of teleprinters and related equipment. A *printer* is a receive only (RO) terminal, also called a *page printer* (not to be confused with the more modern definition). A keyboard is used to create messages. A keyboard with a built-in printer unit is known as a KSR, for *keyboard send and receive unit*. A teleprinter with a built-in tape punch and reader, in addition to a keyboard and printer, is called an ASR, for *automatic send and receive*. A stand-alone tape punch is called a receive only typing reperforator (ROTR). A *reperforator* is a tape punch that receives and decodes its own electrical signal, rather than being mechanically linked to the printer in a teleprinter. A tape reader is known as a *transmitter distributor* (TD). Although these terms are no longer in common usage, it is a good idea to know they exist and what they mean.

The speed at which the 5-level binary Baudot code is transmitted is controlled by a motor in the teleprinter unit. As with Morse code, Baudot RTTY speeds are measured in words per minute (WPM). Timing is very important in RTTY, as with all forms of digital communications. I'll examine the timing characteristics of the Baudot code later in this chapter.

RTTY modems

As mentioned in the previous chapter on radiotelegraphy, CW is sent by keying the transmission of a carrier signal. By keying in the manner prescribed in the Morse code, characters can be sent over radio. RTTY also can be sent in this manner. On/off keying (OOK) is to RTTY what CW is to Morse code. In OOK, the carrier is keyed on and off to transmit the Baudot code. At the receiving end, the timing of the signal on and signal off conditions are used to decode the transmitted message.

The OOK method of transmission leaves a lot to be desired. A strong signal is necessary in order to differentiate successfully between the presence and the lack of a signal. This drawback is very serious when automated decoders are involved. The human ear and brain can decode faded Morse code signals successfully in conditions where a traditional modem would fail. However, RTTY is transmitted at speeds too fast for manual reception, so machines must decode it for us.

In 1953, the FCC authorized the use of frequency shift keying (FSK), which eliminated the problems with OOK. In FSK, two signals are available: one corresponding to the mark and another to the space. Using OOK, the transmitter is keyed to send a mark and unkeyed to send a space. FSK alternates between the two signals, always transmitting a signal. Automatic decoders have a much easier time differentiating between two signals than the presence or absence of one signal.

The FSK signal (technically known as F1B) also can be transmitted using audio frequency shift keying (AFSK). When two tones, corresponding to the mark and space, are fed into the microphone input of an SSB transmitter, the output is identical to FSK. AFSK (J2B) from a properly adjusted SSB transmitter cannot be differentiated from FSK.

The difference between the mark and space signals is known as the *shift*. Several standard shifts are in use in amateur RTTY. The most common is 170 Hz, although 425 Hz and 850 Hz also are used. With direct FSK, the mark frequency is the carrier frequency and the space frequency is the mark frequency minus the shift. With AFSK, two tones that differ by the amount of the shift are fed into an SSB transmitter. The tones must pass through the filters in an SSB receiver that was most probably designed for voice communications, so tones in the 1,000 Hz to 3,000 Hz range are used. Several standard tone pairs are in use and are listed in Fig. 4-1. One important point to note is that in FSK, the higher frequency is the mark, and in AFSK, the higher frequency is the space tone. Therefore, the LSB setting is used to "invert" the tones so that the mark frequency is higher than the space to conform with the standard.

It is possible to receive RTTY using a single-tone demodulator. Demodulators of this type operate on the same basic principle as OOK. By detecting the presence of

Mark	Space	Shift
2125 Hz	2295 Hz	170 Hz
2125 Hz	2975 Hz	850 Hz
1275 Hz	1445 Hz	170 Hz
1275 Hz	2125 Hz	850 Hz

Fig. 4-1. Common standard tone pairs. Those with a mark frequency of 1,275 Hz are known as low tones *and are used by many European and African stations.*

only one of the two signals transmitted by (A) FSK modulators, usually the space signal, the demodulator is able to receive RTTY signals. Although demodulators of this type are simple to design and build, they suffer from the same problems as OOK. Several early solid-state RTTY demodulators used single-tone detectors, but all recent devices demodulate and detect both signals.

The Baudot code

The code that Emile Baudot developed in the 1870s has changed little over the intervening years. The Baudot code is also known as ITA 2, for International Telegraph Alphabet 2. Also, the Murray code, as it is called in England, is nearly identical to the Baudot code. There are many variations in the Baudot code equivalents to accommodate foreign characters, but I'll stick with the standard English language code equivalents. A chart showing the Baudot code and its symbol equivalents is included in appendix B.

The Baudot code is a 5-level code, and as such can only represent a maximum of 32 symbols. Obviously 32 symbol equivalents are not enough to code the alphabet, number, and punctuation symbols in the English language. To get around this hurdle, the Baudot code equivalents are divided into 2 groups, called *cases*: letters case and figures case.

The letters case contains the entire alphabet from A to Z (with no lowercase differentiation). The remaining six open spaces are the same in both cases and include the space character and control characters. Two of these control characters are used to switch between the letters and figures cases.

The figures case includes the digits 0 through 9, punctuation, and other special characters for a total of 26 symbols. These 26 plus the 6 unchanged symbols give a total of 32 symbols in the figures case.

There are several minor differences in the special symbol equivalents between many brands of Teletype machines. For example, where one machine may print a + another machine may print a". However, the vast majority of Baudot decoding equipment follows the code equnivalents shown in appendix B.

Most teleprinters required the operator to actually press a key to switch from letters to figures case and back, but modern electronic Baudot units automatically send the appropriate switch character when a key representing a symbol in the other case is pressed. This is one feature that modern electronic technology has added to make Baudot RTTY more convenient to operate. (We'll explore Baudot RTTY operating techniques later in this chapter.)

The timing characteristics of RTTY are very similar to those of Morse code. There are three main timing elements—the start pulse, the data pulses, and the stop pulse—all of which vary with transmission speed. The start pulse precedes each 5-bit Baudot code stream and indicates the beginning of a new character. The stop pulse follows the 5-bit stream to indicate the end of that character.

Telecommunications systems that use start and stop elements around each individual character code are known as *asynchronous systems*. Because the beginning and end of each character is marked, it is not necessary to precisely time, or synchronize, the transmission and reception of the data.

Without the start and stop bits, the sending and receiving stations must be precisely timed so that the receiving station knows where one character begins and another one ends. Systems that are timed in this manner are known as *synchronous systems*.

The origination of start and stop elements once again traces back to the teleprinter. The motors used in the teleprinters to transmit and receive the digital Baudot code have to be triggered and resynchronized. The start element is used to ready the receiving teleprinter to acquire the next 5 elements that make up the Baudot code of the transmitted symbol. After the 5 elements have been sent to the receiving teleprinter, a stop element is sent to reset the teleprinter (and ready it for the next character).

As was mentioned earlier, Baudot RTTY speeds are measured in words per minute. Additionally, bridging the gap with more advanced forms of amateur digital communications, RTTY speeds are also measured in bauds.

You'll notice many unusual, uneven speeds of Baudot RTTY transmission, again a result of RTTY's teleprinter past. The transmission speeds of teleprinters are regulated by the motor speed and gear ratios, which often results in noninteger transmission speeds. The slowest Baudot RTTY speed is 45.45 baud.

The baud rate is determined by taking the inverse of the shortest element time length. For all of the 45.45 baud transmission rates, the shortest element time length is 22 ms, and 1/22 ms (1/0.022) is 45.45.

Figure 4-2 shows the various standard Baudot RTTY transmission rates. In all cases, the start element is the same length as the data elements. In some cases, the stop element is the same length as the other elements. In the exceptions, the stop length is approximately 50% longer than the start element. By varying the length of the stop bit, the WPM rate can slightly vary while maintaining the same baud rate. These slight variations are known by names such as *Western Union* and *60 speed*. The "speed" designator is a rough synonym for WPM. For example, "60 speed" is actually 61.33 WPM.

The fastest conventional Baudot RTTY speed is 100 baud. The 100-baud transmission rate has a start and data element length of 10 ms (compared with 22 ms for 45.45 baud), and the stop element is 15 ms. The 100 baud equates to approximately 133 WPM. Do not confuse the 100-baud transmission rate with the "100 speed" rate. The "100 speed" rate is 100 WPM, or 74.20 baud.

The WPM rate is calculated using a representative word, 5 characters in length, with a single space character added afterward. The number of times that the word can be sent within one minute is the number of words per minute.

Calculating the WPM is relatively easy. Each character is made up of 5 data elements, 1 start element, and 1 stop element. The total length of each character can be

Baud rate	WPM	Data pulse	Stop pulse	Name
45.45	65.00	22.0ms	22.0ms	Western Union
	61.33	22.0	31.0	60 speed
	60.61	22.0	33.0	45 baud
50.00	66.67	20.0	30.0	50 baud - European
56.92	76.68	17.57	25.0	75 speed
	75.89	17.57	26.36	57 baud
74.20	100	13.47	19.18	100 speed
	98.98	13.47	20.21	74 baud
100	133.33	10.0	15.0	100 baud

Fig. 4-2. The various standard Baudot RTTY transmission rates.

found by adding the elements together. This total is then multiplied by six (for the 5-character word plus the space character) to give the total length of each word. The word length then can be divided into sixty seconds to give the WPM rate. Of course, switching between letters and figures case will add at least one more character (the letters shift or figures shift character), depending on how often it is necessary to switch cases.

Operating RTTY

As you have already discovered, RTTY terminology has developed over time—with much of the terminology relating to equipment that is now obsolete. RTTY operating practices are much the same, however. Much of the operating jargon and techniques of RTTY can be traced to amateur RTTY's beginnings.

The advent of solid-state RTTY systems has irrevocably altered the hardware found in most RTTY stations, but the operating practices are still much the same as they were some 20 or 30 years ago. Some regulatory changes have made RTTY more accessible, such as the FCC ruling that eliminated the need for CW identification of amateur RTTY stations, but the primary reason for the rapid growth of interest in RTTY over the past decade can be traced directly to the ease and convenience of solid-state RTTY equipment.

Regardless of what equipment you are using, the techniques of operating RTTY are the same (although the specific commands used by individual interfaces will vary, of course). In this section, I'll cover some of the basics of RTTY operation so that you can shorten your learning curve and feel more comfortable getting on RTTY. There is no significant difference between Baudot RTTY and ASCII RTTY, so this discussion applies to both—although in reality Baudot RTTY is by far the predominant RTTY mode.

The most common RTTY baud rate and shift is 45 baud and 170 Hz shift (ASCII RTTY is often run at 100 baud). Other common RTTY speeds are 75 and 100 baud, with 100 baud often used by some automated RTTY bulletin board stations. The 425 and 850 Hz shifts are not common in amateur radio use, although many commercial RTTY stations use these shifts. So, the best advice is to start out with your interface unit set to 45 baud and a 170 Hz shift. Your transceiver should be set to LSB (or FSK if your transceiver is so equipped and your interface is wired to the FSK input).

Determining your actual output frequency is usually not very important unless you are trying to tune in a commercial RTTY station for SWLing (shortwave listening) or an inactive amateur RTTY BBS. Often, the listed frequency for these stations is based on the *center frequency* of the transmitted RTTY signal, which is the frequency at the midpoint of the mark and space frequency. The listed center frequency will differ from the frequency display on your SSB transceiver and may well differ from your rig's FSK frequency display.

Many radios with direct FSK will display either the mark or space frequency, not the center frequency. To arrive at the center frequency, you need to know whether your transceiver's FSK display is showing the mark or space frequency, as well as the station's shift. Since the space frequency is always the lowest in frequency, you would add half of the shift to the space frequency to arrive at the center frequency. To find the center frequency starting with the mark frequency, simply subtract half the shift.

When using an SSB transceiver for RTTY, you need to take the shift tone frequencies into account. The standard 170 Hz shift tones are 2,125 Hz for the mark and 2,295 for the space. Since the LSB display will show the frequency of the suppressed carrier, you need to subtract the mark tone from the displayed frequency to arrive at the frequency of the mark signal. From this point you can calculate the center frequency as for FSK displays.

When trying to tune in a commercial RTTY station, RTTY BBS, or simply changing to another frequency, you need to find out what the specified frequency is referring to—the LSB suppressed carrier frequency, the mark frequency, the space frequency, or the center frequency. However, for simple amateur radio RTTY QSOs, you won't have to worry about this since you'll be tuning by ear, most probably with the aid of a tuning indicator.

RTTY operation is very similar to CW in that one station usually calls CQ, another responds, a QSO takes place, and then the contact is terminated. In fact, many CW abbreviations are commonly used on RTTY. Many RTTY stations have prepared text, known as *brag tapes*, ready to transmit at the punch of a key or two. These brag tapes commonly contain a CQ message, biographical information, and equipment lists. These are items that are used in almost every QSO, so rather than having to type them over and over, they are simply retransmitted to new contacts.

In fact, it's usually easy to tell when a brag tape is being sent. Most RTTY operators are not excellent typists, so their real-time transmissions usually trickle in as the operator hunts and pecks on his keyboard, and spelling errors are common. Then when the brag tape starts, the characters start appearing on your screen in a flurry, as if the operator switched places with an experienced secretary, with few, if any, spelling errors. Although brag tapes are no longer small spools of paper tape, they are still very useful, and all serious RTTY operators have a few standard messages saved to disk.

Almost all RTTY QSOs start out with either sending a CQ or responding to one, just like CW. RTTY CQs are typically more detailed than those used in CW, often containing the operator's name and location. Also, RTTY QSOs usually contain the famous string of RYs that amateurs automatically associate with RTTY. In fact, I usually include a line or two of RYs at the beginning of each transmission.

The string of alternating R and Y characters is used because the Baudot code for R (01010) is the inverse of the Baudot code for Y (10101). Thus, the successful reception of these two characters indicates that all of your equipment is operating properly, since all 5 bits are tested. For this purpose, the RY strings only work with Baudot RTTY.

However, the RY strings are also used as a tuning aid. A few lines of RYs at the beginning of each transmission allows the receiving station to adjust his reception precisely without the risk of missing any of the main message. For this purpose, RYs, or any text string, can be used with any non-error-correcting digital code.

Once you have established contact with another station, the QSO continues as usual. For the first few transmissions, you'll probably send your brag tapes and receive those from the other station. After that point, you can continue the conversation by typing in real time. Many solid-state RTTY systems will allow you to type ahead as you are receiving text from the other station. When the other station is finished sending, you can then send the buffered text that you've been typing—a very useful feature.

In addition to standard text messages, many RTTY stations transmit pictures made up of keyboard characters that when printed out look remarkably good from a distance. Some amateurs also transmit computer program code via RTTY, although one of the error-correcting modes would be a better choice.

From the hardware side, since when you are transmitting RTTY the signal is continuously transmitted, you might need to reduce the power output of your transmitter by 50 to 75% to eliminate overheating. Some transmitters are rated for a full duty cycle at their maximum power output, and these rigs should work fine at full power. The smart thing to do is to check the manual and if in doubt, back off on the power.

Conclusion

Many amateurs thought that the advent of packet and AMTOR would make Baudot and ASCII RTTY obsolete. It seems that the opposite has occurred. If anything, interest in the newer digital modes has served to revive interest in operating RTTY, which is the foundation of all digital modes. I'm sure you'll find RTTY a fun mode to operate, and RTTY is an excellent start for the newcomer into the world of amateur radio digital communications.

5

AMTOR

ALTHOUGH CONVENTIONAL RTTY WORKS WELL IN MOST SITUATIONS, ERRORS caused by interference, noise, and fading are common when operating conditions are less than ideal. AMTOR, AMateur Teleprinting Over Radio, is an extension of RTTY that eliminates most errors through the use of redundancy and error-checking. This chapter, will examine the various modes, explain the terminology, and cover the basics of AMTOR operation.

AMTOR was derived from a commercial maritime Teletype system called SITOR, which stands for SImplex Teletype Over Radio. Peter Martinez G3PLX adapted SITOR, described in CCIR Recommendation 476, to the amateur radio service and named the system AMTOR. The FCC approved AMTOR for American amateur radio usage in January 1983.

Amateur usage of AMTOR has grown steadily over the years. The inclusion of AMTOR capability in multimode controllers has greatly increased the numbers of amateurs capable of operating AMTOR. Years ago, hearing an AMTOR station was something of a rarity. Today, AMTOR seems just as common as conventional RTTY.

AMTOR modes

AMTOR is divided into four main modes: A, B, L, and S. Mode A is the ARQ (automatic request) mode; mode B is the FEC (forward error correcting) mode. Mode L is the listen mode, and Mode S is the selective broadcast mode. However, not all AMTOR controllers include all modes, although Modes A and B are the most common.

Mode B is the least sophisticated AMTOR mode and is most similar to conventional RTTY. The forward error-correcting (FEC) system used by Mode B will eliminate many errors that would have occurred with conventional RTTY. Mode A's ARQ system is more complex than Mode B and provides the maximum error-checking in AMTOR. In fact, Mode A is similar in some respects to the advanced error-checking protocols used in packet radio.

Mode S is identical to Mode B with the addition of selective calling, which I'll discuss later in this chapter. Finally, Mode L is used for monitoring AMTOR transmissions. Using Mode L, an AMTOR station can receive Mode A, B, and S transmissions.

Mode B

The most basic AMTOR communications mode is Mode B. Mode B is frequently used for broadcasts to many stations. In Mode B, the FEC system sends each character twice, the second character delayed by 280 ms, following four other characters at 70 ms each. This prevents a static burst or fading from wiping out both characters. The first transmission of a character is known as the DX, and the second transmission as the RX.

At the receiving end, the AMTOR interface buffers the received characters and compares them. If they match, the character is sent on to the terminal. If one character is flawed, most AMTOR interfaces will send the other correct character to the terminal. When both characters are flawed, the interface will send a space character to the terminal, alerting the operator to an error and allowing him the opportunity of mentally inserting the appropriate character based on context, if possible.

In AMTOR, timing is very important, as you've probably surmised by now. AMTOR operates using synchronous transmissions, while conventional RTTY uses asynchronous transmission. As you may recall from the previous chapter, conventional RTTY transmissions have each character framed with start and stop elements. These start and stop elements serve to prime the receiver that a character is arriving and when it has been received. Using the asynchronous system, characters can be sent at random time intervals with no ill effects.

The synchronous system used by AMTOR has no start or stop elements framing individual characters. Rather, a string of characters is transmitted in a precise timing sequence. When there are no characters to send, the AMTOR controller sends idle characters, which maintains the timing sequence without printing at the receiving end.

Mode A

Although the advantages of FEC Mode B are considerable compared with conventional RTTY, Mode A's ARQ system offers increased capability and performance. Unlike Mode B, in which one station transmits and the other(s) receive throughout the transmission, Mode A involves only two stations, which communicate with each other frequently throughout each station's transmissions. This constant communication allows the receiving station to notify the transmitting station if a particular block of characters was not received correctly. The transmitting station then can retransmit the block of characters.

Since the transmitting and receiving stations switch roles so quickly in Mode A, despite the fact that one station is the primary information sender, AMTOR refers to the primary transmitting station as the information sending station (ISS) and the primary receiving station as the information receiving station (IRS). While the ISS is sending information to the IRS, the ISS frequently stops transmitting to listen to the IRS for acknowledgment reports.

While we're on the subject of terminology, the station that begins the communications, or QSO as we amateurs call it, is known as the MS, for master station. The station that the MS is communicating with is the SS (slave station). Throughout the QSO, the MS and SS designators do not change, although the roles of ISS and IRS swap back and forth as the QSO continues.

All of the rapid transmissions between the ISS and IRS and vice versa is what gives Mode A AMTOR its characteristic chirping sound. If you tune around the bands much at all, you've undoubtedly run across this unique sound of Mode A AMTOR. Mode B is somewhat harder to distinguish from conventional RTTY, but after operating AMTOR for a while, you'll be able to tell the difference even if you have difficulty describing how to others.

The ARQ system that Mode A uses operates by transmitting text in three character blocks. The ISS then pauses, switching to receive. The IRS switches to transmit and sends one of two control characters. The first control character indicates that the 3-character block was received correctly; the other requests a repeat transmission of the 3-character block. The IRS then switches back to receive and the ISS back to transmit and either sends the next block of 3 characters or repeats the previous block.

When it's time to switch roles from ISS to IRS and IRS to ISS, the ISS station transmits a special 3-character block (FIGS Z B, also shown as +?, the FIGS equivalent of ZB) which switches the ISS to IRS and tells the IRS to become the ISS. The IRS can also force a switch by sending a special control character in place of the normal acknowledgment control character.

The Mode A QSO is ended by the ISS sending a special termination sequence. The IRS can end the QSO by first forcing a switch to ISS and then implementing the termination sequence. On most AMTOR controllers, the termination sequence is handled automatically.

Unlike Mode B, where transmissions are broadcast, Mode A involves a link between two stations. Thus, there has to be a method of establishing a link, or connection, between the two stations before communications can begin. This is done using the selective call, or SELCAL.

The SELCAL is used in Mode A to signal a particular station. The SELCAL is a 4-character identifier made from the station's callsign. Usually, a station's SELCAL is composed of the first and last three letters of its callsign. For example, if your callsign were KA3GWK, your SELCAL would be KGWK. However, if you have a 1×2 or 2×1 callsign, you would repeat the first letter. For example, my callsign is KR3T, giving a SELCAL of KKRT. This is just the general convention; I could just as easily select KRTT or KRRT.

Now that I've briefly covered the primary modes of AMTOR operation and introduced some important terminology, I'd like to discuss some more technical details before delving into the specifics of AMTOR operation.

Error-checking

By now, you know that AMTOR, in Modes A, B, and S, is able to determine whether characters have been received correctly. Based on this determination, the AMTOR controller will request a retransmission using ARQ or fall back to either the DX or RX (assuming one is correct) in FEC. AMTOR's error-checking system is not nearly as complex as that used in packet radio (which is discussed in the next chapter), but despite its simplicity it is quite effective.

Unlike the Baudot code, the code used by AMTOR is a 7-level code, as is ASCII. But where ASCII has 128 possible character assignments, AMTOR has only 35. AMTOR limits the usable code combinations to those containing four mark units (1's) and three space units (0's), for example 0101011. Out of the 128 total possible codes, only 35 have this unique 4:3 ratio. The complete AMTOR code is displayed in appendix B.

This 4:3 ratio is the heart of AMTOR's error-checking system. All received characters are checked to see if they conform to the ratio. If not, they are obviously in error, and the appropriate action is taken depending on what mode is being used. Of course, it is entirely possible that 2 bits could be altered by noise or fading (as an example, let's assume that 0101011 becomes 1001011). This "mutant" code still conforms to the 4:3 ratio and would be assumed to be correct, even though the ISS meant to send a Y and the IRS received an S.

However, in reality, it is rare to have 2 bits altered in this manner. While the frame check sequence (FCS) used by packet radio is a much more sophisticated error-checking system and would catch this type of error, AMTOR works quite well and errors are uncommon.

Although AMTOR has 35 code combinations, there are actually 38 AMTOR code equivalents. The first 32 codes follow the Baudot code very closely, as I mentioned earlier, and the remaining 3 are used for control and maintenance signals. The remaining 3 code equivalents are simply reassignments of 3 existing codes. These last 3 code equivalents are used as control signals exclusively by the IRS in Mode A. This works since the IRS decodes these codes as text characters while the ISS decodes them as control signals (since the IRS can't send text without first becoming the ISS).

Modulation and timing

The modulation system used by AMTOR is very similar to conventional RTTY, so much from chapter 4 applies here. AMTOR uses the standard 170 Hz shift, but there is only one speed used: 100 baud. Because AMTOR is a synchronous system, timing is important. In AMTOR, the precise timing of transmissions is necessary, especially in Mode A. As I mentioned earlier, each character takes 70 ms to transmit, and a block of 3 characters takes 210 ms.

Mode A is much more demanding of timing considerations than FEC. The AMTOR standard specifies that blocks be sent and acknowledged within 450 ms (or 2.222 blocks per second). It takes 210 ms to send the block of 3 characters, and 70 ms for the IRS to send the 1-character control signal. This leaves 170 ms for transceiver switchover time and propagation delay.

Propagation delay is more important than might be initially assumed. Since radio waves travel at 300 km per ms, every 300 km between the two stations will take up 2 ms of time (1 ms each way). Assuming absolutely no transceiver switchover delay, all 170 ms are available for propagation delay, yielding a maximum possible distance between stations of 25,500 km, or 15,845 miles. Thus, long-distance direct communications (such as some satellite and moonbounce) are not possible.

Of course, in the real world, transceiver switchover time from transmit to receive and vice versa is another factor to consider. For a transceiver to work well with AMTOR ARQ, it must have a switchover time of less than 20 ms. Most modern solid-state transceivers have switchover times of about 10 ms. Assuming a switchover time somewhere between 10 and 20 ms, the maximum direct distance for AMTOR Mode A works out to a little over 20,000 km (12,427 miles).

In most situations, Mode A will work without problems. When distances or switchover times begin to get in the way, it's time to switch to Mode B, since the FEC used by Mode B does not have the stringent timing requirements of Mode A's ARQ.

Although AMTOR's data transmission rate is 100 baud, its actual data throughput is much lower because of the repetitive nature of AMTOR. Of course, the presence of errors resulting from poor band conditions will cause throughput to slow even more. So, don't expect ASCII RTTY throughput from an AMTOR station.

Operating AMTOR

AMTOR can be more intimidating than conventional RTTY to many new users. In this section, I cover some basic operating techniques that you should keep in mind when getting started in AMTOR. Much of your operating specifics will depend on the capabilities of your particular AMTOR interface, so be sure to read your manuals thoroughly before attempting on-the-air communications.

After your interface has been wired to your terminal and transceiver, your first step into AMTOR operating is to program your SELCAL into your interface. Once you're sure your interface is up and running properly, you should try some Model L monitoring. Tune to the RTTY/AMTOR bands listed in appendix E and listen for the characteristic "chirp-chirp" of Mode A ARQ. You also can try copying the ARRL bulletins transmitted using Mode B (check a recent issue of QST for the W1AW bulletin schedule).

Once you can successfully monitor AMTOR communications, you are ready to begin a QSO. Most stations will call CQ using Mode B and include their SELCAL in the CQ message. AMTOR CQs are very similar to those in conventional Baudot RTTY, so just follow that format. You can tune around in Mode B looking for a CQ or find a clear frequency and call CQ yourself.

Assuming you've found someone calling CQ, you can either contact that station using Mode B or Mode A. Most AMTOR operators jump right to Mode A, but many newcomers feel more comfortable sticking with Mode B in the beginning. If you're using Mode B, be sure to follow the RTTY guideline of turning down your output power unless your transmitter is rated for full-power RTTY operation. Since Mode A transmits in such short bursts, you can go ahead and run it at full power, but I think you'll find that with AMTOR you don't need a lot of power for reliable communications.

To contact a station using Mode B, simply switch to transmit and start typing. Mode B is very similar to conventional RTTY operation, so much of the RTTY operating guidelines apply here. The other station will probably continue the QSO in Mode B or might try to initiate a Mode A connection, assuming you've sent your SELCAL.

Any AMTOR station can initiate a Mode A connection. Simply follow your interface's commands to input the station's SELCAL and everything will take place automatically. You should observe your transmitter keying up briefly and then hear the other station chirping back at you. Once this happens, press your carriage return key twice. Many AMTOR units will not display typed text until it has been received successfully by the IRS, so when you notice your terminal screen scroll up twice, you know that your carriage returns were received properly.

At this point, you are the master station (MS) since you initiated the contact, and you are also the ISS since you are currently transmitting to the other station. You can now proceed with the QSO. When you're ready to swap places with the other station, send the +? code to reverse the roles of ISS and IRS. How you go about sending this code varies on different AMTOR interfaces, so check your manual. However, simply typing it on the keyboard usually will work.

The process of terminating the contact again varies among units. After following the procedure particular to your interface, your transmitter should chirp a few times then fall silent. You might then have to exit the ARQ mode or switch to Mode B or Mode L to continue AMTOR operations.

AMTOR vs HF packet

Over the past few years there have been many debates over which is the best error-checking HF mode: AMTOR or HF packet. Each has their advantages, but in my opinion, AMTOR has the edge for general-purpose HF RTTY QSOs. As you'll learn in the next chapter, packet is much more sophisticated than AMTOR and does not perform as well under poor band conditions. I'd gladly use HF packet under ideal conditions, but in the real world, AMTOR works better.

APLink

APLink stands for AMTOR-Packet Link, and is a system developed to take advantage of the advantages of both systems. Basically, APLink is a gateway between an HF AMTOR station and a VHF packet station. It allows a VHF packet station to communicate over HF using the advantages of both packet and AMTOR. From the other side, an AMTOR station can connect with distant VHF packet stations. Using APLink, distant AMTOR users can send messages over the packet BBS network described in the next chapter. Most of the APLink stations are about 14,070 MHz to 14,080 MHz, so monitor in that general area. Once you've found one, you can monitor other users to learn its capabilities and operating practices.

NAVTEX and AMTEX

Another interesting AMTOR-like system is NAVTEX. NAVTEX is really a SITOR system used by the maritime industry to gather weather and navigation information. NAVTEX broadcasts on 518 KHz, below the standard AM band, using FEC. In the United States, the U.S. Coast Guard originates NAVTEX broadcasts. There are 5 or so NAVTEX transmitters in and around the U.S., so the odds are good that you will be able to copy one.

NAVTEX transmissions have a special header that identifies the particular bulletin. Compatible NAVTEX receivers can then ignore future repeats of the same bulletin.

The advantages of a NAVTEX-like system to amateur radio AMTOR bulletins is obvious. Thus, the term AMTEX has been recently coined to describe NAVTEX-type bulletin broadcasts on the amateur radio bands. The manufacturers of AMTOR interfaces will have to modify their units' firmware to work with the AMTEX system, although regular FEC will work fine for general reception.

Conclusion

AMTOR is an excellent advance in RTTY technology. Mode B provides the same operating style as conventional RTTY with the advantage of error-checking. Mode A provides the advantage of error-correcting in a sophisticated, yet easy to operate, system. And AMTOR is continuing to advance as demonstrated by the developments of APLink and AMTEX. One recent change in the AMTOR specifications that has been approved by the FCC is an additional 7-character SELCAL known as an IDENTITY. It allows the slave station to determine the callsign of the master station that connected. However, manufacturers will have to modify their firmware to take advantage of this new capability.

While AMTOR is continually evolving, numerous users are enjoying its present capabilities every day. Once you give AMTOR a try, I'm sure you'll find it quickly becoming your favorite HF digital mode.

6
Packet radio

WHAT FOLLOWS IS JUST A QUICK OVERVIEW AT THE ALMOST ENDLESS VARIETY OF operating situations that are typical in amateur packet radio.

Amateur packet radio was used effectively during the 1984 Summer Olympics in Los Angeles. Packet stations were set up to forward telephone messages rapidly across long distances. The system was successfully operated 24 hours a day for more than 11 days. In the end, more than 1,300 messages were sent. (See Fig. 6-1).

When northern California suffered a devastating flood in February 1986, amateur packet radio proved to be a welcome addition to the usual array of emergency communications provided by volunteer amateur operators. Packet radio was used throughout the flood to provide direct communications with a variety of emergency service organizations, including the California Department of Forestry and the American Red Cross.

Through a network of packet remote bulletin board stations and packet repeaters, emergency traffic could be routed to almost any specific destination in the disaster area. Packet radio offered several important advantages over other systems commonly used in the past. Packet was error-free and much faster than ordinary radioteletype. Packet did not require that the messages be recopied by hand when received, nor did the messages have to be retyped when sent to another site. The use of bulletin board stations allowed all sites the flexibility of getting their messages at convenient times without having to man the packet station continuously.

Packet radio also was used for emergency communications immediately after the Amtrak train wreck near Baltimore, Maryland, in January 1987. A portable packet station was set up near the wreck site and messages were sent to a local packet bul-

Fig. 6-1. The packet station used at the 1984 Summer Olympics in Los Angeles.

letin board station. At the bulletin board station, an operator forwarded the messages via both packet and voice.

Amateur packet radio was put to use to handle the emergency traffic during the aftermath of the 1988 earthquake in Armenia. At the request of the Amateur Radio Emergency Communications Organization of the U.S.S.R., the ARRL organized the shipment of 6 portable VHF packet stations to the U.S.S.R. The equipment was donated by Tandy, Yaseau, and AEA.

Amateur operators are now beginning to realize fully the potential of packet radio for emergency traffic handling. The systems in use should grow more efficient as amateurs gain more experience with packet in emergency situations.

Amateur packet radio is used every day by ordinary amateur radio operators the world over, with equally spectacular results. Individuals can transfer messages via packet almost anywhere in the United States through a network of bulletin board stations with an automatic forwarding system. Individuals can use their local bulletin board to send or receive mail, upload and download files (such as newsletters and computer programs), and as a gateway to retransmit their signal on another frequency. Imagine instructing the bulletin board to relay your transmission on the 20-meter band. An amateur in Pennsylvania running only 5 watts on 2 meters could then communicate with another amateur on the West Coast or in a foreign country (Fig. 6-2).

Many packet operators can share a single frequency and select the stations with which they wish to communicate. It is not uncommon to have an operator using a bulletin board system while two other operators are conducting a QSO and another two are transferring computer programs—all on the same frequency.

Some amateur packet operators access amateur satellites directly to relay their transmissions to specified points around the globe. Amateur packet operators without satellite capability can access the satellites through an intermediary station known as a *teleport*.

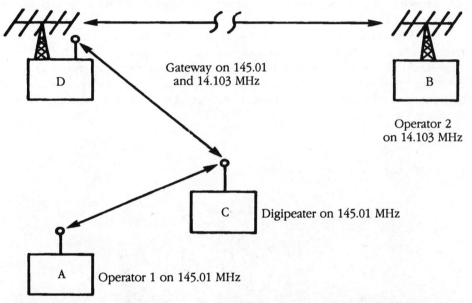

Fig. 6-2. A diagram of a packet radio network in which a digipeater (station C) and HF gateway (station D) are used to allow station A on 2 meters to communicate with station B on 20 meters.

Introduction

At first glance, packet radio can seem very complicated and confusing. A common assumption is that a packet operator must be an expert in digital electronics and computer programming. Although that was probably true during the early periods of packet radio development, packet has advanced to the point where a complete packet station can be set up and operated effectively by almost anyone. For the microcomputer hobbyist, packet represents an ideal marriage between computers and amateur radio.

But we're getting ahead of ourselves. What exactly is packet radio and what does it have to offer? The purpose of this chapter is to provide an introduction to packet radio's capabilities. Amateur packet radio is a complex digital communications system that uses a high degree of computer technology to obtain a reliable, versatile means of communicating information. Despite the high degree of technology involved in packet radio, it is an easy mode to operate. Packet radio is being routinely used for error-free rag-chewing, program and information transfers, and satellite and computer communications.

TNC

The terminal node controller (TNC) is the heart of a packet station. The TNC serves as an interface between a user's terminal and the packet radio network. The TNC is also known as a packet controller, a packet assembler/disassembler (PAD), and a frame assembler/disassembler (FAD).

The TNC is responsible for organizing and controlling the transmission and reception of data across a packet radio network. The two kinds of TNCs are software-based and hardware-based. Some TNCs are a mixture of the two, with some functions being handled by hardware and others by software. Today, however, the term *TNC* usually applies to a hardware system. A collection of various TNCs is shown in Fig. 6-3.

Fig. 6-3. Assorted TNCs. Clockwise from the bottom: the original VADCG TNC, the Pac-Comm TNC-200, the Kantronics KPC-2, the AEA PKT-1, the Heathkit HD-4040, and the VADCG TNC+. The disk contains the Richcraft AX.25 TNC software system.

Software-based TNCs

The best known software-based TNC is the Richcraft system. It is a complete packet system, with the exception of modem and transceiver, written for use on microcomputers based on the Z-80 microprocessor, specifically the TRS-80 Models I, III, and IV. For more information on the Richcraft system, see chapter 9.

In theory, a software-based TNC has several advantages over a hardware-based one. No additional hardware beyond the microcomputer and modem is needed, so the total system cost is reduced. Total power consumption is also reduced because the TNC software does not consume any extra power beyond that normally required by the computer. A software-based system makes maximum use of the available resources.

However, a software-based system does have several crippling disadvantages. It is machine dependent, so the software is limited as to what computer configurations it will work with. It is also expensive and time-consuming to develop software for a range of machines. With the wide proliferation of microcomputers, it would be all but impossible to develop software for each one. A software-based system puts stringent demands on the computer system. Since tasks must be carried out within very tight time frames, very efficient design criteria for both the software and computer must be met. Some computers simply lack the capability to handle a software-based TNC.

By using a software-based TNC, you restrict yourself to the user interface provided within the software. The user interface is your access to the packet system. Commands and other information are entered and received using the user interface, and if it is not convenient to use, you will either get used to it, suffer with it, or attempt to modify the software. Most user interface options are available for hardware-based TNCs.

For these reasons, software-based TNCs have not become very popular. However, they do work and provide an inexpensive means to get on packet, provided you have a compatible computer and modem available.

Hardware-based TNCs

Hardware-based TNCs are the mainstay of the packet marketplace. Many manufacturers have jumped on the packet bandwagon, and now there are numerous hardware-based TNCs available that vary in price and performance. However, one TNC has established itself as the de facto standard: the TAPR TNC-1. The TAPR standard was reenforced and expanded by the TAPR TNC-2. As explained in chapter 2, TAPR had a fundamental role in the development of packet radio in the United States and the world. Until the TNC-1 was discontinued by TAPR, over 2,500 units were sold.

The TNC-1 contains many features not found on present day TNCs, such as a parallel status port and a wire wrap area on the circuit board for customized prototypes. It is an experimenter's board, but also sets the stage for "plug and chug" appliance-type operating. Its user interface has become a standard, and because of TAPR's liberal licensing agreements, many commercial TNCs are direct copies of TAPR's design.

A hardware-based TNC is actually a microcomputer system. As you will soon see, it contains the same basic components as a microcomputer. Although different

ICs might be used in different designs, the basic functions remain the same. No matter how many extras are added on, a TNC must have several standard capabilities in order to function properly.

Asynchronous I/O   All hardware TNCs must contain some sort of I/O capability for terminal communications. This is usually in the form of a serial communications port conforming to the RS-232 standard. (More information on the RS-232 standard can be found in appendix D.) Through the I/O port(s), the TNC accepts data and commands and sends and receives data and status messages.

The RS-232 serial I/O has become the standard for most peripheral communications. A *peripheral* is any component that is added on to a computer system, such as a printer, modem, and, of course, TNC. In serial I/O, the information in the form of bits is transferred serially one bit at a time over a data line (Fig. 6-4). Other lines are usually included for control and for carrying status information.

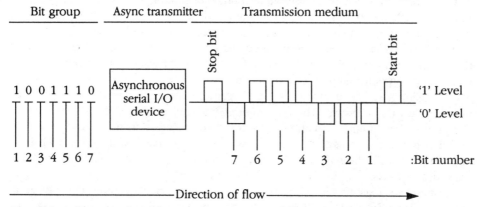

Fig. 6-4. A diagram showing asynchronous serial data transmission.

Almost all microcomputers and terminals provide for RS-232 communications. To connect a peripheral to a terminal or computer using an RS-232 interface, a 25-wire ribbon cable is usually used for runs under 50 feet. The ribbon cable is usually terminated on each end with a DB-25 connector, which is the "standard" connector in RS-232.

Parallel I/O also is used for connecting peripherals to computer equipment. Today it is used almost exclusively for connecting printers. In parallel I/O, the information bits that make up each piece of data are sent at the same time over individual wires (Fig. 6-5). For example, if each piece of data is represented by one byte, 8 bits, then 8 separate wires would be used. Other wires are added for carrying control and status information between the computer and the peripheral. Parallel I/O is not used much in most TNC designs.

Parallel transfer is used internally in most computer systems and TNCs to transfer information between its components. For example, information is transferred between the processing unit and memory in parallel. Thus, a means of converting from parallel to serial and back again is needed to communicate with the outside

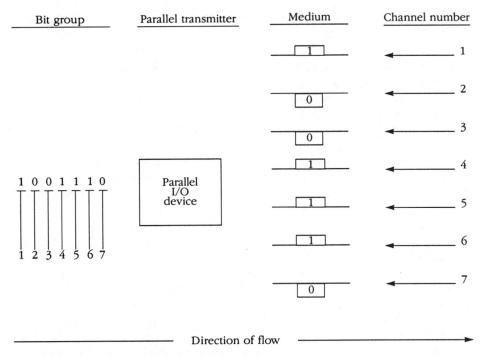

Fig. 6-5. A diagram showing parallel data transmission.

world through a serial port. This conversion is accomplished through the use of a Universal Asynchronous Receiver and Transmitter (UART).

The UART takes information fed to it in parallel format and sends the information out in serial format. In reverse, the UART accepts serial data and converts it to parallel format. UARTs are found in almost all serial communication I/O circuits.

Memory   Memory is another component that all TNCs share. Random access memory (RAM) is used for storage of short-term information, such as variable parameters, and as a buffer for receiving and sending frames. Since RAM loses its contents when power is removed from it (volatile memory), some form of backup is usually provided in the form of a small battery cell on the circuit board to maintain power to the RAM at all times. One other method of backing up the RAM is used in the TNC-1: a special kind of nonvolatile RAM for storage of valuable information. Most TNCs come equipped with a minimum of 16K (16,384 bytes or 131,072 bits of information) of RAM.

Read Only Memory (ROM) is another form of memory found on most all TNCs. The ROM is actually Programmable Read Only Memory (PROM), which is programmed, or "burned in," with the permanent programs needed to run the TNC. The programs consist of the user interface, the protocol(s), the calibration routines, and any other programs necessary to use the features of the TNC. Some TNC manufacturers put user information such as callsign and VADCG number in ROM. Communications with the TNC is through the user interface. It accepts commands and displays status information.

The protocol(s) implementation programs that are contained in ROM usually consist of the AX.25 protocol, and the VADCG protocol in some older TNCs. These two protocols, along with a discussion of protocols in general, are covered later in this chapter. The protocol contains the rules to keep track of each frame and controls the transmission of frames.

The amount of ROM that comes with a hardware TNC varies depending on the number and complexity of programs included, but is usually 8K to 32K. ROM is an ideal medium for storing long-term information, and it can be removed easily for upgrading should a new version come out.

HDLC   So far you know that the information or data to be transmitted comes from the I/O port and that the program that controls the transmission of the frames is contained in ROM. But where does the information that comes into the TNC via the I/O port for transmission get put into frames and actually sent? This is the job for the high-level data link control (HDLC), and one of its functions is to format data into frames for transmission. It generates the frame check sequence (FCS) of outgoing frames. If you recall from chapter 1, the FCS is the root of packet's error-checking. The HDLC also disassembles and checks the FCS of received frames. Some TNCs handle the HDLC functions in software, while others use a separate IC designed especially for HDLC functions.

CPU   Just as the TNC is the heart of a packet station, the CPU is the heart of the TNC. It manages the operation of all other components and serves as a clearinghouse for all data transferred between components. The CPU follows the instructions programmed in ROM.

The speed with which the CPU performs its tasks is controlled by the system clock. The system clock generates all timing signals for the CPU and other components. Along with the capabilities of the components, the system clock puts an upper limit on how fast the TNC can work.

Radio I/O   After the HDLC has assembled a frame for transmission, the transmission is sent to the modem. The modem circuit is usually, but not always, included on the TNC circuit board. If it is not included on the board, an I/O connector is provided on the TNC to interface with an external modem. TNCs with on-board modems should have an external modem connector or some way to bypass the on-board modem should it be necessary to add an external modem. This feature is desirable to accommodate greater filtering if needed or a change in the standard modem specifications used for packet radio.

TNCs with on-board modems usually include a calibration program so it is easy to calibrate the modem without extra equipment. An on-board modem is a great convenience; however, a TNC without a way to bypass the on-board modem easily can cause problems if the modem standards change significantly. Modem standards and digital modulation techniques are covered later in this chapter.

Although information usually comes to the TNC in asynchronous format from the terminal, the information in packet form is sent to the modem in synchronous format. In synchronous communications, there are no start and stop elements surrounding each bit group. Rather, the bit groups are combined into one long bit stream and sent as a whole (Fig. 6-6). Because the sending speed and length of bit groups are predefined, the receiving station is able to identify the individ-

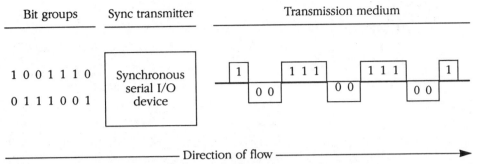

Fig. 6-6. A diagram showing synchronous serial data transmission.

ual bit groups without the use of start and stop elements. However, the receiving station must know when the bit stream starts and when it ends. Thus a special character, called a *flag*, is usually inserted at the beginning and end of each bit stream.

Power requirements   The power requirements of hardware-based TNCs vary from around 20 mA to 1A and up at 9 Vdc to 12 Vdc. If you are planning to operate a portable packet, current drain is an important criterion to keep in mind. Sometimes the power consumption of a TNC can be reduced by replacing regular MOS (metal oxide semiconductor) chips with their CMOS (complementary MOS) equivalents when possible. CMOS chips draw much less power. Most TNCs today are designed to run on 12 Vdc.

TNC system trace

Now let's do a trace of a hardware TNC based on the knowledge we have of its components. Assume that a terminal of some sort is connected to the I/O port, that a transceiver is connected to the modem, and that the modem is on-board or interfaced in some way to the board (Fig. 6-7). Some introductory information about the formation of a frame is given in this section. More detailed information on this process is provided later in this chapter.

The first trace is the path of an outgoing packet through the system. The information to be transmitted to the receiving station is typed on the keyboard of the terminal. The information goes through the I/O port into the TNC and is directed by the CPU to a RAM buffer as controlled by the software in ROM. Once the maximum length of the information field is reached or a send frame command is received from the terminal, the information is sent to the HDLC, along with other control data. The HDLC combines the control data and the information into a frame and then computes the frame check sequence. The FCS is added to the end of the frame.

The completed frame then is sent to the modem, where the individual bits from the HDLC modulate the signal sent to the transmitter. The transmitter then transmits the modulated frame to the receiving station, usually in less than a second, provided the link between the two stations is clear and reliable.

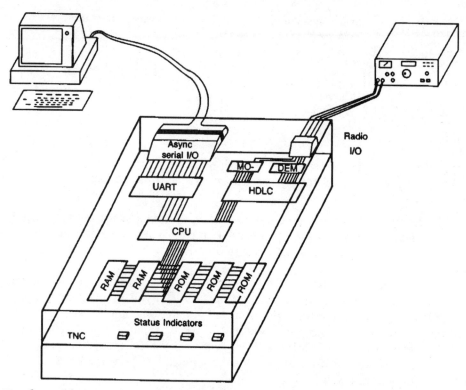

Fig. 6-7. A blowout of a hardware TNC illustrating the various components.

The receiver at the receiving station receives the modulated frame and sends it to the modem. The modem demodulates the frame and sends the bits to the HDLC. The HDLC then disassembles the frame into its component parts—control data and information—provided the FCS check is good.

The information is then routed to the terminal I/O or RAM if the port is busy, as directed by the CPU following the program in ROM. The information is sent through the I/O port to the terminal, where the information is displayed exactly as it was sent.

Each frame is sent this way. Whether you are transmitting a short note to your friend down the street or a large file across town, it all goes one frame at a time.

Amateur packet radio modulation schemes

In the early days of amateur packet radio—the late 1970s and early 1980s—packet experimenters were looking for modems to use with their systems. They had to be cheap, reliable, and plentiful. The modems also had to be simple; experimenters were having enough problems with the TNCs alone. The modems had to have a fairly high baud rate and be easy to interface with the rest of the system. They chose the Bell 202 standard because it met all these requirements.

Bell 202 modems are still found as surplus items and at hamfests for very low prices. The Bell 202 standard uses a 1,000 Hz shift with mark and space tones at 1,200 Hz and 2,200 Hz. They can handle the standard 1,200-baud rate of VHF packet radio and are easy to calibrate and use.

The Bell 202 modem was implemented in packet radio for use with 2-meter FM transceivers. The modulation method used is AFSK at 1,200 baud. Bell 202 modems are the type found on most on-board TNC modems and usually uses a phase lock loop (PLL) demodulator.

A PLL demodulator works by using a phase detector along with a voltage-controlled oscillator (VCO) in a feedback circuit. A direct-current feedback voltage is generated proportional to the difference in frequency between the received audio and the VCO. This voltage changes as needed to adjust the VCO to the same frequency as that which was received. Therefore, the voltage will vary as the input audio frequency alternates between mark and space conditions. This varying voltage is then filtered and amplified to produce the required mark and space signals.

There are several disadvantages to using PLL demodulators. One is that they tend to lock onto the strongest signal in their lock range, often ignoring weaker signals that you might be trying to copy. Another disadvantage is that a PLL has no variable tuning indicator, so it must be tuned by ear in conjunction with a single LED, which lights when a signal is tuned in.

However, these disadvantages are not too important on VHF and UHF. The fact that the PLL tends to lock in on the stronger signal is useful if two stations transmit at the same time. The stronger signal might be received correctly, thus avoiding a complete collision. Also, since most packet activity on VHF and UHF takes place on preassigned fixed frequencies, tuning is not a major issue.

For HF operation, shift-filter-based modems usually are used. The filters are tuned for particular shift frequencies and come in 2 different kinds: passive and active. A passive filter is a simple LC resonant circuit whose bandpass is preadjusted to pass the necessary frequency pairs. An active filter system, either transistors or ICs, might use feedback filters or switched capacitor filters to provide the desired bandpass characteristics.

There is an increasing amount of packet activity on the HF bands. The 10-, 20-, 30-, 40-, and 80-meter bands are being used for transcontinental and DX communications. There are HF gateway stations, which allow for input on VHF using the Bell 202 standard and output on HF. Thus, a modest station or one without room for an HF antenna can take advantage of the increased range of HF.

Because of the characteristics of HF operation, different modem configurations have been developed for packet transmission. The usual standard is 300 baud (A)FSK with a 200 Hz shift. If AFSK is being used, the LSB (Lower Side Band) is chosen. On 10 meters, the Bell 202 standard is sometimes used.

Although Bell 202 on VHF is the mainstay of packet activity and HF is being increasingly utilized, other forms of modulation have been under development and will see increasing usage in the future as a result of their obvious advantages. For amateur satellite activity, 400-baud FSK is being used. For high-speed linking 9,600-baud PSK and FSK is under development, and very high speed (56,000 baud) radio modems are under development for real-time digitizing of voice and video along with high-speed linking.

Radios

In order for a transceiver to work well on packet radio, it must meet several requirements. A fast turnaround time from transmit to receive and vice versa (T/R time) is important for efficient packet operation. A slow T/R time will reduce the throughput of the packet network. A T/R time of 50 milliseconds is fine and up to 100 milliseconds is tolerable. Radios with T/R times from 5 to 15 milliseconds are ideal. Since the transceiver will most probably be left on for long periods of time, good stability is a necessity. Most modern rigs do not have a problem in this area.

The transceiver's bandwidth must be capable of passing the audio tones used in modulation. Low distortion is another desirable feature. The relative amplitude of modem tones should not be altered significantly by the radio. Changes in phase are tolerable as long as the change is linear (all frequencies shifted the same amount).

Don't let these requirements worry you too much. Almost any recent transceiver is adequate for packet operation. On VHF FM, a hand-held will do. HF operation is somewhat more critical of transceiver performance; a modern synthesized rig is recommended.

Network basics

A single packet station is useless for communications. In order to communicate, 2 or more stations are needed. Although this problem is not encountered much these days, in the early days of amateur packet radio many operators would rush to put their packet station together only to find out that there were no other packet stations in their area.

When there are 2 or more packet stations within communications range of each other, a network is formed. In digital communications, a *network* can be defined as a collection of communications devices linked so that one station can communicate with any other station on the network. The difficulty with networking is deciding on implementing a system that allows for maximum flexibility and throughput while minimizing complexity and cost.

In the simplest case, a packet network consists of a few stations within direct communications of each other on a single frequency (Fig. 6-8). A more complex network involves *digipeaters* (simplex packet repeaters) to extend a station's communication range and gateways for accessing stations with different capabilities, such as those on another frequency or using another modem standard (Fig. 6-9).

However, this system is not ideal in many respects because of congestion, range limitations, and other problems. Before more advanced work can be done dealing on packet networking, additional work has to be done in the area of protocols. The present-day packet system has stretched the current protocols to their limits, and much work is being done in the area of developing protocols.

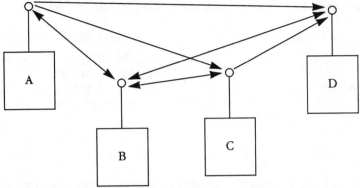

Fig. 6-8. A diagram of a simple network in which all stations can communicate with each other directly.

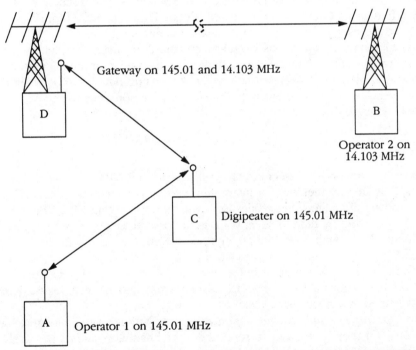

Gateway on 145.01 and 14.103 MHz

Operator 2 on 14.103 MHz

Digipeater on 145.01 MHz

Operator 1 on 145.01 MHz

Fig. 6-9. A diagram of a more advanced network, in which a digipeater (station C) and HF gateway (station D) are used to allow station A on 2 meters to communicate with station B on 20 meters.

Multiplexing

Since packet operation today occurs on agreed-upon single frequencies, a method of allowing stations to access the frequencies in an orderly manner is necessary. If each station transmitted whenever it wanted to, collisions and other problems would occur. There must be a way to allow each station to use the frequency (channel) without interfering with other users.

The method used is known as *multiplexing*. Multiplexing allows a group of users to share a communication medium. In its ideal form, each user is not aware that he is actually sharing the channel. It should seem, from the user's perspective, that he is the sole user of the channel. Two forms of multiplexing immediately concern amateur packet radio operators: time division multiplexing (TDM) and frequency division multiplexing (FDM).

FDM

FDM allows each transmitting user to have a separate channel for communications. A good example is the radio stations on your FM stereo. Each station has its own frequency and occupies it continuously. In an active two-way communications system such as amateur radio, it would be wasteful to assume that each station could have its own frequency. Usually a set number of frequencies is allocated for communications, and the user selects one before initiating communications.

Usually, once a station has begun to communicate over a certain channel, it remains on that same channel for the duration of the communications session. This method is known as *static FDM* because the stations do not switch between different frequencies during a connection. Pure FDM operation does not provide a very versatile network.

TDM

Since many users share a common channel, we turn to TDM to allow each user to access the same channel without interfering with other users. In TDM, each station transmits one after the other while users with no traffic stand by. Thus, the frequency is allotted by time to users with traffic to send; one station transmits for a time period, and when it is through, another station transmits. Let's discuss how a station knows when it is OK to transmit.

There are 3 popular systems in use that control the access of individual stations to a communications channel: *polling, token passing*, and *random access*. Random access is used in amateur packet radio.

In a *polling system*, a master station asks each station on the network channel individually if they have traffic to send. If so, the channel responds positively and then transmits. The channel is kept clear of other traffic since no other station has been cleared by the master station to transmit.

Another form of TDM similar to polling systems is *token passing*. In a token passing system, a single electronic token (a special binary sequence) is passed from station to station until it arrives at a station that has traffic to send. The station holds onto the token and transmits. The frequency is kept clear because only the station with the token is allowed to transmit. When the station has finished transmitting, it passes the token to the next station on the network. Depending on the configuration of the network, individual stations may communicate with each other directly or via the master station.

One reason polling systems have not become popular in amateur packet radio is that they require a master station, which must have a fairly powerful computer and reliable communication to all network users to keep track of the users and their status. Because of the nature of amateur packet radio, users tend to drop in and out quickly and the radio links between stations vary in quality. In order for a polling network to work effectively, network conditions must be regimented beyond what most amateurs can provide due to the increased cost and high reliability needed. Another reason polling has not been proposed more for amateur packet radio is the amount of overhead required. The concept of *overhead* will be discussed later; however, a quick definition is the amount of information that must be added to the basic data in order to route the data to its destination.

The system used in amateur packet radio today is random access. In a random access system, each individual station accesses the network as it sees fit under a defined set of rules. Each station must be able to determine if the channel is fit to be used; i.e., clear. In amateur packet radio, the method used is known as *Carrier Sense Multiple Access with Collision Detection (CSMA/CD)*. Each station monitors (senses) the channel and when the station has traffic to send, it checks to see if the channel is clear. If the channel is clear, the station transmits. A successful transmission is indicated by the reception of an acknowledgment from the destination station. If the channel is not clear, the station waits until the channel is clear and then transmits.

If two or more stations transmit at the same time, a collision may occur. If a collision does occur, no acknowledgment is received by the stations involved in the collision, so each waits a random length of time and then attempts to retransmit. One station has a shorter random wait than the others and captures the channel first, thus avoiding another collision (at least with the stations originally involved in the collision).

Packet radio uses both FDM and TDM in order to permit many users to transmit and receive simultaneously. The channel (frequency) selected by FDM affects both the range and speed of data transmission. For example, channels in the 20-meter band have a large range but limited speed, and channels in the 2-meter band have a limited range but support much higher speeds.

TDM allows multiple users to share the same channel. CSMA/CD is used to implement TDM. One important point to keep in mind about CSMA is that all the stations on the channel must be within hearing range of each other for it to work for all stations. Figure 6-10 shows the difference between FDM and TDM.

SDM

This introduces a new kind of multiplexing: *space division multiplexing (SDM)*. SDM comes about because all stations cannot hear all other stations. SDM becomes increasingly applicable as higher frequencies with limited ranges are used. It lets 2 operators use the same radio channel at the same time without interfering with each other. For example, a station in California can transmit on 145.01 MHz at the same time as a station in Pennsylvania, and because the 2 signal paths do not cross, they can coexist without any problems. In essence, they are not on the same network. SDM can result from a variety of causes including propagation, radiation patterns, and physical obstructions. In the VHF and UHF bands, such effects are fairly constant and can be predicted quite easily.

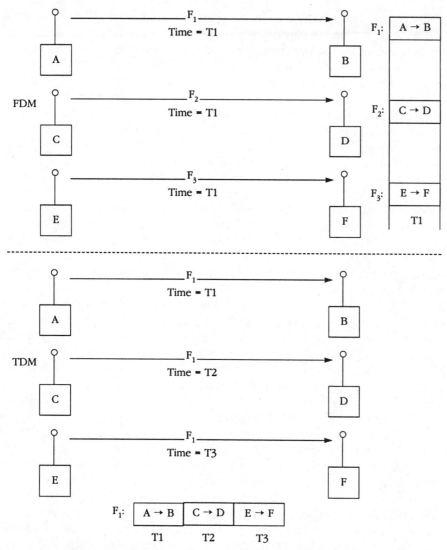

Fig. 6-10. A diagram illustrating the difference between FDM and TDM. In FDM, all three transmissions occurred simultaneously on separate channels. In TDM, the three transmissions occurred sequentially on a single channel.

Amateur packet radio multiplexing model

By combining the effects of FDM, TDM, and SDM, it is possible to develop a packet radio multiplexing model. Imagine a layer cake with thin layers. Each layer represents a different frequency, and the area of each layer is proportional in size and shape to the total geographical area of the network. The cake has a large number of layers, each layer representing a packet radio channel. Individual stations operating at certain frequencies are represented on the appropriate layer by points placed at the proper geographical location. The range of a station is plotted around that station's location. The size and shape of the range (coverage) plot depends on the frequency used, the amount of power the station is transmitting, the gain and directionality of the antenna, and propagation conditions. Differences in transmit and receive coverage are not taken into account for the sake of simplicity.

If the range plots of two stations overlap on the same layer, they can communicate directly. If the plots do not overlap, a digipeater or gateway might have to be used to bridge the gap. If the range plots of two or more groups of stations (networks) do not overlap, the groups of stations can operate as independent networks concurrently without interfering with each other. If the range plots between two groups of stations do not overlap, they are not independent and TDM must be implemented to share the channel. This model can be applied to local as well as wide area networks by simply extending the total area that each layer of the cake represents. See Fig. 6-11 for a graphic representation of these concepts.

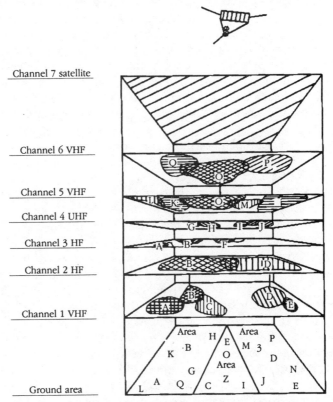

Fig. 6-11. A model representing the present-day amateur packet radio multiplexed network. Stations B, D, and O are gateways that allow stations on one layer to communicate with stations on another layer. By spreading the total number of stations over several channels, the congestion on a single channel is reduced. Notice the wide coverage of the satellite channel.

Protocol basics

Now that we've discussed the basic networking concepts and a physical picture of the packet radio network you have, we can take a look at the intelligence behind the systems that are implemented to make packet radio work. How do individual stations know how to communicate with each other? What happens if data is sent, but for some reason is not received? What if the data arrives garbled? How does a station know if received data is meant for it? How do digipeaters know to retransmit certain data, but not others? The answers to these questions and many more are found in the *protocol* used.

A protocol is a predefined series of steps that are followed to accomplish something. Protocols define how data is to be packaged and what actions are to be taken under certain conditions along with when the actions are to be executed. The ultimate goal is to get data from the originating station to the destination station as quickly and efficiently as possible with no errors. The general steps involved in communicating using packet protocols are discussed in the following section.

Assuming that a station can access the network and reach other stations, it must let a station know that it wants to communicate. In packet radio, this is known as a *connect request*. If the selected station is available, it acknowledges the connect request and the 2 stations are connected. Once the stations are connected, the information they send to each other is received error free. And when the 2 stations are finished communicating, they must disconnect from each other and be ready to connect to other stations.

All of these processes and many more are handled by *protocols*. A simple example that illustrates how a random access packet radio protocol works in a normal 2-meter FM phone contact.

First, you call the station you wish to communicate with. (AA3F, AA3F this is KR3T. Do you read me?) At all times throughout the communication, you first listen to see if the frequency is clear before transmitting. You keep calling until he responds or you get tired and give up. Assuming he responds, you have now established a connection. (KR3T this is AA3F. Go ahead.) You would then transmit the information you wish to communicate. (AA3F this is KR3T. Meet me at the mall in 5 minutes.) Notice that you send the receiving and sending station's callsigns so that AA3F knows this message is for him. (The FCC likes it, too!) If AA3F responds, or acknowledges (KR3T this is AA3F. Roger.), then you know the message was received. If AA3F does not respond within a reasonable length of time or asks KR3T to repeat the message, you retransmit the message until he acknowledges it or you get tired and give up. The connection is ended by sending a disconnect request. (AA3F this is KR3T. 73.) AA3F responds. (KR3T this is AA3F. 73.) You have just ended the connection and are now free to communicate with another station if you wish.

A good example of a polling protocol is a 2-meter repeater net. In a repeater net, the repeater is used as the primary station. All individuals transmit to the repeater and the repeater relays the signal to the other users. One user is designated *Net Control Station (NCS)*. The NCS acts as the equivalent of an amateur radio central node or master station.

The NCS is responsible for initiating the net by calling for stations to join in (the equivalent of logging onto a central node). The NCS maintains a list of those stations currently in the net. After the net has begun, new stations must call the NCS and request to be included.

Referring to the list of stations currently logged into the net, the NCS calls each station individually and asks if they have any traffic to send (the equivalent of polling). If the station does have traffic, the channel remains clear while the polled station transmits. After the polled station has finished transmitting, or if the polled station does not have any traffic, the NCS polls the next station on the list.

The NCS assumes all stations on the list are operating unless the station does not respond to a poll or requests to be excused from the net. In both cases, the station is deleted from the list. If one station is considered to be of more importance than the others (i.e., emergency traffic), it might be polled earlier and more than once in each cycle through the list.

The same basic systems apply to packet radio. A connection is established, information is transferred (sending information again when it is not received properly), and the connection is canceled. Keep in mind that these are very simple generalizations. The protocol must be able to determine when information is received incorrectly, keep track of the connection's status, translate data, ensure device compatibility, and much more. A more detailed look at the way protocols are organized and the kinds of protocols in use in amateur packet radio follow.

OSI/RM

Any network, packet or not, is made up of a multitude of different components and functions (i.e., terminals, codings, voltages, error-checking, connections, relays, and disconnectors). Networks can become very complex as their capabilities increase, and numerous approaches are possible. To alleviate some of the complexity, the *International Standards Organization (ISO)* developed a reference model for networks, known as the *Open Systems Interconnection Reference Model (OSI/RM)*. (*Open systems* are systems that are available for communications, like a packet radio station.) The OSI/RM is designed to facilitate the exchange of information between systems. A system can be as simple as a current loop teletype and as complex as a worldwide network. The OSI/RM separates network functions into different levels based on their purpose.

Each OSI/RM level transfers data between the level directly above and directly below it in the level hierarchy. The point at which data is transferred between levels is called the *interface*. Data originates at the highest implemented level and is passed down serially through each level, where the data is processed by that level's protocol, until it reaches the lowest implemented level. When the data is received, the path of the data is reversed and the data is sent up the levels, where each level removes whatever additional information was added by that level's equivalent at the sending station. By the time the data reaches the level from which it was originated, it looks exactly the same as when it was entered into the network.

Each level operates independently of the other levels. The only exchange of information between levels occurs at the predefined interface points. Each level has a protocol associated with it. One level's protocol can be changed without affecting the rest of the levels. The set of levels and associated protocols form the network architecture.

The OSI/RM is the basis on which the amateur packet radio network is being developed. Its flexibility and structure are great helps in maintaining compatibility among packet systems. The OSI/RM is divided into 7 levels (layers). Each level is responsible for particular tasks and has been assigned a name representative of its function.

The seven OSI/RM layers are: physical, data link, network, transport, session, presentation, and application. (See Fig. 6-12).

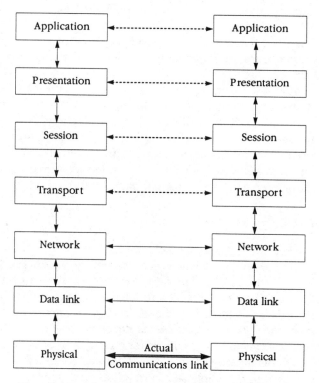

Fig. 6-12. The levels of the OSI/RM. The solid arrows indicate layers that must be implemented at each node. The layers indicated by dashed arrows must be implemented only at the originating and destination nodes.

1. Level 1 is the physical layer. It is responsible for the transparent transmission of bit streams across the physical interconnection between systems. The physical connection can be operated in either simplex, half duplex, or full duplex. The bits must arrive in the same order in which they were sent. Specifications for the physical layer include mechanical (such as plugs and dimensions), electrical (such as voltage levels), and procedural (such as rules and sequences).

2. Level 2 is the data link layer. The data link layer is responsible for shielding the higher levels from the characteristics of the physical layer. It provides reliable, error-free transmission of data. The data link layer should contain some form of error detection and correction. The data link layer also must be independent of the data sent; it may not alter the data in any way. It must accept data and break it into segments for transmission. When the segmented data is combined with protocol information, a frame is formed. The frame must be *delimited* (i.e., allow for recognition of the beginning and end of the frame) and transparent (looked at only as a series of bits).

   The frame must be checked for errors upon reception and sent again by the last station that has a copy of the frame if an error was found. The frames must be delivered in the same order that they were sent. The data link layer is responsible for a great deal. The standard level 2 protocol is *high-level data link control (HDLC)*. A subset of the HDLC is used in most amateur packet radio data link layer protocols. The data link layer used in packet radio is discussed in detail later in this chapter.

3. Level 3 is the network layer. It is responsible for providing transparent transfer of all data submitted by the transport layer (level 4). The network layer completely relieves the transport layer from any concerns about the way in which the communicating systems are connected. The systems might be connected point-to-point (direct) or might have many systems (nodes) in the path. The network layer must provide the necessary routing functions necessary to get data from one system to another in the network; each system may act as a relay. The actual routing methods are not covered in the OSI/RM. Level 3 of the X.25 standard is one standard protocol for the network layer.

4. Level 4 is the transport layer. It is responsible for arranging the information in the correct order in the event the packets arrive out of sequence. The transport layer is only concerned with communications between the originating and destination stations, and not with any relay stations that might be used by the network layer.

5. Level 5 is the session layer. The session layer is responsible for initiating and terminating communications between stations on the network.

6. Level 6 is the presentation layer. The presentation layer is responsible for data transformation (e.g., converting ASCII to Baudot), data and display formatting (for example, a graphics terminal communicating with a hardcopy teleprinter), and syntax selection. If the two communications systems are using incompatible devices, the presentation layer handles the conversions necessary for the 2 devices to transfer data.

7. Level 7 is the application layer. It is responsible for the proper operation of *application entities,* or user-oriented software. Any programs or computer functions controlled by the connected system would be located at the application layer and fall under the control of its protocol(s).

Amateur packet radio protocols

This section describes the levels of the OSI/RM as they relate directly to amateur packet radio. The levels currently implemented in amateur packet radio in the United States are the physical layer, the data link layer, and rough forms of the network layer. Other levels and protocols currently under development are also discussed.

Physical layer

The physical layer is fairly well standardized. The Bell 202 and Bell 103 are the most widely used modulation standards. The RS-232C asynchronous serial interface is another physical layer standard. Other modulation standards will emerge as high-speed modems and new modulation schemes are developed.

One area of the physical layer regarding the transmission of data that is specified in the physical layer is *encoding technique*. The encoding technique defines the format of the modulated signal. In ordinary RTTY, as well as present-day amateur packet radio, a *bipolar format* is used. In bipolar keying, 2 different signaling levels are used for the representation of binary 1 and 0. Bipolar keying is an improvement over *unipolar keying*, in which a single tone is used to represent a binary 0. (See Fig. 6-13.)

There are several forms of bipolar keying. The one that is used by regular Baudot RTTY and AMTOR is known as *non-return to zero (NRZ)* or *NRZ-Level (NRZ-L)*. In NRZ, a binary 1 is represented by one level or tone, and a binary 0 is represented by another level. Thus, if the data being transmitted is the binary grouping of 1001110, the signal switches (transition) from a level representing the binary 1 to the level representing the binary 0, remains at the binary 0 level, switches back

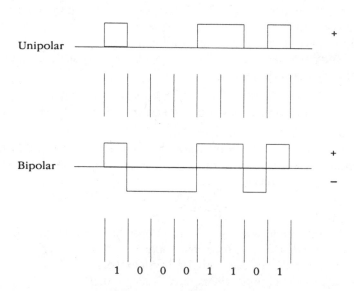

Fig. 6-13. A diagram showing the differences between unipolar and bipolar keying techniques.

to the binary 1 level, remains at the binary 1 level for the next 2 bits, and then switches back to the binary 0 level for the last bit.

The bipolar method currently used by almost all packet radio stations and supported by all the manufactured TNCs is known as *NRZ Inverted (NRZI)* or *NRZ Space (NRZ-S)*. In NRZI, a binary 0 causes a switch (or transition) between signal levels, while binary 1 remains at the current level. The signal levels are not referred to as "binary 1 level" and "binary 0 level" because these terms have no meaning in this encoding technique. Instead, the 2 signal levels are called *mark* and *space* levels. The same binary sequence, 1001110, is sent, starting at the mark level, switches to the space level for the next bit, switches to the mark level for the next bit, remains at the same level for the next 3 bits, and then switches to the space level for the last bit. (See Fig. 6-14).

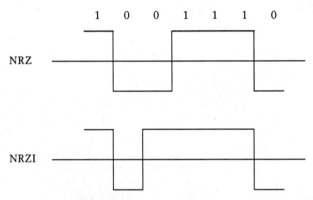

Fig. 6-14. A diagram showing the differences between
the NRZ and NRZI encoding techniques.

Other forms of bipolar keying encoding techniques are *NRZ-Mark (NRZ-M)*, the opposite of NRZ-S, *pulse position modulation (PPM)*; pulse duration modulation (PDM); and Manchester I and II. For more information on these and other encoding techniques, see pages 19–39 in the 1986 *ARRL Handbook*.

Data link layer

The data link layer is also standardized in amateur packet radio. The AX.25 protocol is the most common, and is supported by almost all commercial TNCs. The V-1 (VADCG), and V-2 are also data link layer protocols, which differ from AX.25 in many respects. All three protocols are based on the HDLC ISO standard. Therefore, let's start off with a look at HDLC.

HDLC   HDLC is an acroynm for *high-level data link control*. The HDLC is the data link layer (level 2) of X.25 and is defined in the following ISO standards: ISO 3309, ISO/DIS 4335, ISO/DIS 6156, and ISO/DIS 6259. HDLC is responsible for delivering error free data through the network. HDLC also isolates the upper levels from the physical layer. Data is broken up into blocks (frames) for transmission. The *user data*, the actual data being sent through the network by the users, is called *data* or *information*.

HDLC consists of 3 sublayers:

- transparency of the bit stream
- frame format
- cooperation between stations

Before going any further with the discussion of HDLC, let's digress for a moment and explain the differences between COPs and BOPs.

COP is an acronym for *character-oriented protocol*. Examples of COPs include ANSI X3.28 and IBM Binary Synchronous Communication. In a COP, the data being sent must be represented as characters of specified length, usually 7 or 8 bits (one byte). Thus, there is a limit to the type of information that can be transmitted. All transmission lengths must be a multiple of the specified character length. COPs are fine as long as only text is being transmitted. But packet radio is designed to be capable of sending any type of digital data including characters of different lengths, graphics, and special formats. In packet radio, it is also necessary to condense the size of the transmissions as much as possible.

This is where *bit-oriented protocols (BOPs)* come in. A good example of a BOP is HDLC, along with the amateur packet radio data link layer protocols. BOPs allow for the transmission of any format of digital data. If control information is only 3 or 4 bits long, it only consumes 3 or 4 bits, not a full 7 or 8 as in COPs. Now, back to HDLC.

Transparency of the bit stream   The first sublayer of HDLC, transparency of the bit stream, means that all data being transmitted must look the same. No special-length bits or signaling elements can be used. All data should pass through the physical layer without any altering or processing. HDLC must be independent of the data sent; however, HDLC must also delimit (mark the beginning and end of) frames.

Delimiting is accomplished by the use of flags. A *flag* is a special binary sequence found only at the beginning and end of a frame. The flag used in HDLC is 01111110. This flag must not appear anywhere else in the frame.

To keep flags out of the user data, the data is examined, and a 0 is inserted after every five 1 bits found in a row. This process is called *bit stuffing*. The receiving stations correct for this by removing the bit after a sequence of five 1s if it is a 0; if the bit is a 1, it does not, since the sequence of 1s is part of a flag.

Frame format   In the second sublayer, the frame format, all data is segmented and sent in frames, which are delimited by flags. The components of the frame between the two flags consist of addresses, control information, data, and the *frame check sequence (FCS)*. Figure 6-15 shows the HDLC frames.

The first frame component following the initial flag is the *address*. The address in HDLC consists of the address of the originating station and the destination station. The addresses are usually numeric; however, AX.25 uses callsigns as addresses and includes digipeaters in the address section.

The next section (or field) in the HDLC frame is control information. Control information can consist of several things, depending on the type of frame. There are 3 types of frames defined under HDLC: information, supervisory, and unnumbered. The control field consists of 8 bits.

HDLC frame construction

Information	Flag (8)	Address (8)	Control (8)	Information (8X)	FCS (16)	Flag (8)

Unnumbered and Supervisory	Flag (8)	Address (8)	Control (8)	FCS (16)	Flag (8)

Fig. 6-15. The HDLC frames. The numbers in parentheses indicate the total number of bits in that particular field. The information field is usually a multiple of 8 bits.

Information frames are used for data transfer (they carry user information). Bit 1 of the control field of an information frame consists of a binary 0; bits 2 through 4 represent the transmitting station sequence number (often called transmit count); bit 5 is the poll/final bit; and bits 6 to 8 represent the receiving station sequence number (receive count).

Supervisory frames are used to control the flow of data. Bit 1 of the control field of a supervisory frame consists of a binary 1; bit 2 is a binary 0; bits 3 and 4 represent the supervisory frame type indicator; bit 5 is the poll/final bit; and bits 6 to 8 represent the receive count.

Unnumbered frames are used to control the link. Bits 1 and 2 of the control field of an unnumbered frame consist of binary 1's; bits 3 and 4 are modifier bits; bit 5 is the poll/final bit; bits 6 to 8 are also modifier bits.

Each station involved in a link maintains counters for the number of information frames sent and received. These counters are known as the *sequence number*, or *count*. The counters are sent in the control field of each information frame and are used to check the sequence of received frames and to acknowledge the reception of frames.

The poll/final bit is used to indicate that the receiving station must acknowledge the frame.

The last component of an HDLC frame, next to the final flag, is the FCS. The FCS is a *cyclic redundancy check (CRC)* performed on a frame. The FCS is an error-detection scheme in which a check character is generated by dividing the entire numeric binary value of a block of data by a generator polynomial. The FCS value is sent along with the data, and at the destination station, the FCS is recomputed from the received data. If the received FCS matches the one generated from the received data, the data is considered error-free.

The FCS is computed starting with the first bit after the opening flag and ending with the last bit preceding the FCS. For more detailed information on the FCS methods, see ISO standard 3309.

Cooperation between stations   The last sublayer of HDLC, cooperation between stations, is handled by special frames that are recognized by HDLC as commands and responses. These command and response frames are used to establish connections, acknowledge receipt of frames, handle disconnections, and perform other tasks. Specific information about the different commands and responses used by HDLC to manage the link layer are not given here. The commands and responses utilized in amateur packet radio are discussed under the appropriate protocols.

AX.25   The AX.25 protocol was originally developed by AMRAD, and after some minor modifications, AX.25 became the standard level 2 protocol in amateur packet radio. The AX.25 protocol is very similar to the level 2 protocol of the X.25 standard; thus, the name "AX.25" ("A" is for amateur). This version of AX.25 filtered around for awhile, and minor incompatibilities existed among various implementations. In 1984, the ARRL Ad Hoc Committee on Amateur Digital Communications finished a revised version of the AX.25 standard.

The ARRL-sponsored version of AX.25 is known as AX.25 Version 2 to differentiate this version from earlier versions of the same protocol. The earlier AX.25 protocol is now known as AX.25 Version 1. The most popular, and thus standard, AX.25 Version 1 protocol is the one developed by TAPR. Although there are some incompatibilities between the two versions of AX.25, they are very similar.

AX.25 follows the same frame format as HDLC. The main differences are that the address field has been extended to allow for amateur radio callsigns as addresses and that unnumbered information frames (unnumbered frames containing user data) can be transmitted.

Following is a brief description of the various components of an AX.25 frame (See Fig. 6-16).

AX.25 frame construction

Information and unnumbered info	Flag 8	Address 112 → 560	Control 8	PID 8	Information ≤ 2048	FCS 16	Flag 8

Supervisory and unnumbered	Flag 8	Address 112 → 560	Control 8	FCS 8	Flag 8

Fig. 6-16. The AX.25 frames. The numbers in each field indicate the number of bits contained in that field. The address field can contain a minimum of 112 bits (two callsigns at 56 bits each) and up to 560 bits (two callsigns plus eight digipeaters). The largest information field is 2048 bits.

The flag is identical in function and design to that used in HDLC.

The address field consists of a minimum of one amateur radio callsign belonging to the sending station in an unnumbered information frame (the destination address is set to a dummy address). In most cases, the destination station's callsign is included. Up to 8 digipeater callsigns also may be added; thus, the maximum number of callsign addresses in the AX.25 address field is 10.

Each callsign consumes 7 groups of 8 bits (8 bits = 1 byte = 1 character, also called an *octet*). Callsigns are made up of uppercase ASCII characters and numbers. The first 6 characters are allotted for the actual callsign; if the callsign is less than 6 characters in length, spaces are added to the end. The seventh character is the *substation identifier* or *secondary station identifier (SSID)*. The SSID ranges from 0 to 15. Only 4 bits of the 8 available for the SSID are consumed. The first and last bits are set to 0 and the remaining 2 are reserved for future use.

The SSID of a digipeater carries additional information. The last bit of the SSID is set to 1 once the frame has been digipeated by that station. This step is necessary to avoid a digipeater repeating a frame twice.

The control field is made up of 1 octet. It is used to identify the type of frame (information, unnumbered, unnumbered information, and supervisory). It also contains the frame count numbers used for acknowledgments and special signals for establishing and maintaining connections (commands and responses).

A *protocol identifier field* (PID) is included with frames containing information. It is used to identify what kind of network layer protocol, if any, is being used.

The information field contains the user data being transmitted. The field is usually divided into a multiple of octets; the maximum being 256.

The FCS is the same as that used in HDLC.

Each transmission is usually preceded by a series of 16 alternating bits to allow the receiving station time to synchronize onto the signal.

AX.25 is actually a subset of the HDLC standard as it does not implement the full range of features defined in HLDC. AX.25 is based on the LAPB subset of HDLC. (*LAPB* is an acronym for *Link Access Procedure Balanced*.)

In a "normal" HDLC network, there are usually several slave stations (user terminals) linked to a central controller (host system; also called primary or master station). The master station usually contains more "intelligence" than the slave stations and is better able to manage the link. This configuration, with one intelligent master station linked to a less intelligent slave station, is called *unbalanced* because the stations do not possess equal capabilities.

In amateur packet radio, we want each station to be equal to any other station in terms of capability. Thus, no master or host station is used. The links between stations are in a balanced configuration. This type of station arrangement is supported by LAPB under HDLC.

Let's take a look at the actual frames used by AX.25 to establish connections, and acknowledge frames and disconnects.

Unnumbered frame control fields are either commands or responses. They are used to handle all communications between stations when no connection has been established. There are 6 different unnumbered frames defined in AX.25.

SABM   The first unnumbered frame is a command called SABM, an acronym for *set asynchronous balanced mode*. It is used to send a connect request to another station. The control field in this frame contains a special sequence of bits that identify it as a SABM frame. The SABM command is used to place two stations in asynchronous balanced mode (meaning they are connected).

DISC   The next unnumbered frame is also a command. It is known as a DISC frame. The *DISC* frame is used to send a disconnect request to another station, terminating the connection between the two stations.

DM   The *disconnected mode* unnumbered frame is a response. It is sent whenever a station receives any frame other than a SABM while disconnected. It is also sometimes sent in response to a SABM frame to indicate the station is not available for connection.

UA   The *unnumbered acknowledge* unnumbered frame is a response. It is sent as an ACK for unnumbered frame commands. A received command is not executed until a UA frame has been sent.

FRMR   The *frame reject* unnumbered frame is a response. It is sent when a frame is received that cannot be processed by the station (the frame is not garbled, but is not a valid frame). This response is usually sent when a frame clears the FCS check, but is not recognized by the station's protocol. Some situations that might cause this include the reception of a command or response not defined in the protocol or an information frame whose information field exceeds the maximum allowable length.

UI   The *unnumbered information* frame is an addition to the X.25 protocol included in AX.25. The UI frame allows for the transmission of an information field without the establishment of a connection first. These frames are not acknowledged.

Once a connection is established using these commands and responses, it is up to AX.25 to handle the error-free transfer of information between the two stations. This process is accomplished through the use of supervisory frames. There are 3 supervisory frames defined in AX.25.

RR   RR is an acronym for *receive ready*. RR is a response used to indicate that the sending station is able to receive information frames, to acknowledge the reception of information frames, and to clear an RNR response (see next paragraph) previously set by the station. The RR frame acknowledges the reception of information frames by including the receiver count, indicating what frames have been correctly received. The other station can examine the count and update the next frame to be sent according to what frames can be forgotten.

RNR   RNR is an acronym for *receive not ready*. The RNR is a response used to indicate that the sending station is temporarily busy and is not able to accept any more information frames. This situation might occur when the receive station's receive buffer is full; it sends an RNR to the other station telling it to hold any information frames until the receiving station is able to receive more frames. The RNR condition can be cleared by sending a UA, RR, REJ, or SABM frame.

REJ   REJ is an abbreviation for *reject*. The REJ frame is a response that is sent to request the retransmission of information frames that were received out of sequence. The frame(s) to be retransmitted are indicated by the receive count in the control field of the frame. The REJ condition is cleared by the proper reception of the requested frames.

AX.25 protocol trace   Let's trace the steps taken by AX.25 when connecting and disconnecting from another station. When a user types C KR3T at the command prompt and presses the RETURN key, the TNC prepares a SABM frame containing the user's call and KR3T in the address field. The TNC then checks to see if the channel is available (CSMA). If so, the SABM frame is transmitted.

KR3T receives the frame and finds its call in the destination address. If CONOK is ON and the TNC is free to establish a connection, KR3T sends a UA frame to the originating station and enters the connected mode. If CONOK is OFF, KR3T sends a DM frame to the originating station.

Assuming KR3T is available and the originating station has received the UA frame from KR3T, it also enters the connected mode. Information frames are now used to transfer information between the two stations. The receive and transmit counters are kept current by the two stations.

The RR frame is used to acknowledge the reception of information frames. If a frame is received out of sequence by one of the stations, it sends an REJ to the other station and the frame is retransmitted.

When one of the stations wants to end the connection, he returns to the command mode and enters D at the command prompt. His TNC then sends a DISC frame to the other station. The other station sends a UA frame acknowledging the disconnect request and then enters the disconnected mode. Once his station receives the UA frame, it also enters the disconnected mode.

This concludes the section on the AX.25 link layer protocol. You might have noticed a few points about AX.25 that do not seem to fit in with the earlier description of the data link layer given earlier in the chapter. These discrepancies include the addition of digipeaters and the use of end-to-end acknowledgments. Digipeaters seem to fall under the control of the network layer protocol, not the data link layer. In many respects this is true.

However, keep in mind that digipeaters are not full-fledged level 3 network nodes by any means. They are a simple kludge added to allow for rudimentary networking. The user must select the digipeaters used; the TNC does not contain automatic routing tables or other means of independently selecting digipeater routes. Most likely, digipeaters will eventually fade out as more advanced network nodes and level 3 protocols emerge.

As for the end-to-end acknowledgments, in the OSI/RM they would seem to be the responsibility of the transport layer (level 4). The transport layer is responsible for the proper reception of frames from one station to the other through the network. However, in AX.25 no network layer protocol is yet implemented, so the point-to-point acknowledgments of the data link layer were simply extended over the digipeater path. If the digipeaters are eliminated from the path, the acknowledgment returns to a point-to-point ACK as used by the data link layer. True network nodes use point-to-point acknowledgment between nodes and a transport layer acknowledgment between the two end stations.

For more detailed information on the AX.25 protocol, I recommend the following sources:

- *The TAPR TNC-1 System Manual*
- "AX.25 Amateur Packet-Radio Link-Layer Protocol" from the ARRL
- "Proceedings of the Second ARRL Amateur Radio Computer
- Networking Conference" from the ARRL

V-1   The next packet protocol we will examine is V-1. The V-1 protocol is more commonly known as the VADCG protocol. It was developed by Doug Lockhart VE7APU in late 1979. In the summer of 1979, Lockhart was working on a protocol for the VADCG TNC, which was designed for use with a master station and multiple TNCs. The TNCs would connect to the station node where they would be assigned numeric addresses, and all communications between users would take place through the station node.

A packet group in Hamilton, Ontario, was working on developing TNCs, and wanted a protocol that allowed the TNCs to be connected to each other directly, rather than going through a station node. They asked Lockhart if he could provide them with such a protocol so that they could concentrate on experimenting with the TNCs, rather than having to set up a station node first.

Lockhart complied with their request by modifying the protocol he was using, eliminating the dynamic addressing and other facilities used by the station node. The result was a simple protocol that allowed TNCs to connect to each other directly; a kind of kludge to meet a specific request.

Well, this temporary experimental protocol grew in popularity because it was distributed with VADCG TNC kits and eventually spread to the United States. This protocol is commonly called the VADCG protocol. Now that Lockhart has completed work on a second VADCG protocol, the original VADCG protocol has been named V-1.

The V-1 protocol achieved widespread use in the United States because it was the only protocol around that actually worked at the time. Lockhart never intended for it to become a standard, but with nothing else around it became a *de facto* standard. However, the VADCG protocol in use in the United States was not exactly identical to the one that Lockhart developed for the Hamilton packet operators.

The VADCG protocol as it was first used in Canada allowed for up to 254 numeric addresses. Each station would have one numeric address assigned beforehand. When Hank Magnuski KA6M put the United States' first all-digital simplex packet repeater (a digipeater) up on December 10, 1980, in California, he used a modified version of the VADCG protocol to allow for digipeating. Hank used a portion of the address space to support digipeater control, thus reducing the total number of user addresses from 254 to 32.

This modified version of VADCG protocol used in California became the standard in the United States. Lockhart was approached several times about making the VADCG protocol an international standard. However, he consistently resisted the idea because he still saw the VADCG protocol as a temporary testing protocol that was too limited for widespread use. These limitations later would cause packet groups in the United States to develop alternate data link level protocols such as AX.25

The VADCG protocol had only 2 commands: connect and disconnect. To connect with another station, the user would type its callsign and a CTRL-X. A connect request frame would be sent containing the other station's call, the user's call, and the user's VADCG numeric address. The other station would respond with an acknowledgment containing this VADCG numeric address. From then on, all information frames would be sent with only the VADCG addresses. To disconnect, the user would type a CTRL-Y and a disconnect request would be sent. Once the disconnect request was acknowledged, the connection was terminated.

The VADCG protocol is still in limited use today in Canada and Australia. The VADCG protocol is very similar to HDLC, since numeric addresses are used in both. The VADCG protocol will not be explained in detail, as it is no longer in widespread use and is of limited use to most packet operators.

For more detailed information on the VADCG V-1 protocol, I recommended the following references:

- *The TAPR TNC-1 System Manual*
- Early issues of *The Packet Newsletter* from VADCG

V-2   Doug Lockhart has continued with the development of link-level protocols since he does not feel that AX.25 is a viable link-level protocol for the large-scale development of packet radio for various technical reasons. The next VADCG protocol he developed is known as V-2. It offers many improvements over the V-1 protocol.

Both full- and half-duplex links are allowed. Multiple links are supported, along with some multiple protocol support. The number of numeric addresses has been increased significantly, and no coordination of the address is needed beforehand.

When the specifications of V-2 were published, TAPR compared them with the AX.25 protocol and found some notable variations, but not enough of a difference to necessitate changing the current link-level protocol. Some of the differences between V-2 and AX.25 are that V-2 offers reduced address space, differentiation between user names (callsigns) and node addresses (numeric identifier), and no "network-level functions.

V-2 is similar to SLDC, HDLC, AX.25, and V-1. V-2 is designed to be implemented along with upper-level protocols to establish a complete network. For more information on the V-2 protocol, I recommend the following references:

- "Proceedings of the Third ARRL Amateur Computer Networking Conference" from the ARRL
- *The Packet Newsletter*, Issue 9: October 1984, from the VADCG

Other level 2 protocols   There have also been several other data link-layer protocols in use in amateur packet radio over the years. Two Canadian groups, other than the VADCG, developed viable packet systems with their own protocols. TAPR developed its own link-level protocol known as TAPR/DA prior to the adoption of AX.25

One of the Canadian groups based in Montreal was using a combination COP/BOP protocol using ASCII characters as frame delimiters. Its system was operational in 1978, running at 4,800 baud AFSK on 220 MHz.

A second Canadian group based in Ottawa was using a polling protocol and first developed the concept of a digipeater. Its system was running at 9,600 baud FSK in 1980.

The order of the very active early Canadian groups is Montreal in 1978, Vancouver in 1979, and Ottawa in 1980.

For more information on the additional Canadian systems, I recommend the following references:

Montreal:

- *Packet Radio* by Rouleau VE2PY and Hodgson VE2BEN, TAB Books (#1345).
- "The Packet Radio Revolution" by Rouleau VE2PY, *73 Magazine*, December 1980.
- "An Introduction to Packet Radio" by Hodgson VE2BEN, *Ham Radio Magazine*, June 1979.

Ottawa:

- Early issues of *The Packet Newsletter* from the VADCG.

TAPR had a data link-level protocol up and running shortly after its founding. It is known as TAPR/DA for TAPR/Dynamic Addressing. It was being implemented before the 1982 AMSAT/AMRAD protocol conference and was one of the protocols considered. However, it was passed over in favor of AX.25 during the conference.

Network layer

Current protocol work in the United States is being directed toward level 3 network layer protocols. There are several systems under development today. Most of the protocols are based on the level 3 of X.25.

At their current stage, these systems simply acknowledge packets being repeated through them (they replace the end-to-end ACK of AX.25 with a point-to-point ACK). In the near future, they should contain routing tables that will select automatically the best route for a packet to reach its destination, transparently to the user.

Another more recent networking system is NET/ROM developed by Ron Raikes WA8DED and Mike Busch W6IXU. This protocol simply replaces the ROM chip in any TNC-2-compatible TNC and turns the TNC into a networking node. Users can connect to other NET/ROM nodes, as well as conventional stations, with the benefit of point-to-point ACKs through the NET/ROM nodes. It also maintains routing tables to other local NET/ROM nodes so it is not necessary to specify a path between nodes. Numerous NET/ROM nodes are now operating all over the country.

A TAPR project is a *Network Node Controller* (*NNC*). The NNC is a combination hardware and software device designed to serve as a network node in an amateur packet network. It is actually a small, but powerful, computer system, complete with microprocessor, memory, and external storage. It contain's four HDLC ports with very flexible characteristics.

Two ports might be configured for Bell 202 use on VHF, a third for 9,600 baud on UHF, and the fourth for Bell 103 on HF. Thus, a user may connect to the NNC on one port and route his packets out one of the other ports (this may be handled automatically by the NNC's software). The NNC will acknowledge frames as they are received (a point-to-point acknowledgment).

The network layer (level 3) is usually divided into two distinct sublevels: 3A and 3B. Level 3A is controlled by the *intranet* protocol and 3B is controlled by the *internet* protocol. The intranet protocol deals with communications around a single network node and user stations. The internet protocol deals with communication between network nodes.

Communications between individual users and their network node (intranet) will most probably be accomplished through *virtual circuits*. A virtual circuit is a method of connecting stations in which an abbreviated address field is used once a connection is established. The stations must be connected before communications can begin. After the connection is established, the addressing information contained in each transmission is decreased. However, the lack of complete addressing information forces each packet to take the same path through the network.

Communications on the internet are still under debate. They may be virtual circuits or possibly datagrams. A *datagram* is a method of connecting two stations in which each packet sent over the network contains complete addressing information. The advantage of datagrams is that they can be dynamically routed through the network (i.e., the path of the connection can change) because they contain complete addressing information. The advantage of virtual circuits is that once the connection is established, the amount of packet space consumed by the address field can be reduced significantly.

Virtual circuits require more reliable, intelligent network nodes to remember the path of the connection. Datagrams can reach their destination despite the failure of one or more network nodes by being dynamically routed around the nonfunctional nodes.

Once network nodes are implemented fully, a user from one area of the country can access a node and connect to any other station that the network reaches (similar to the telephone system). More information on possible network architecture is given in chapter 10.

For more information on level 3 networking, see the "Proceedings of the Third ARRL Amateur Radio Computer Networking Conference" from the ARRL and the 1985 or 1986 *ARRL Handbook*, chapter 19, from the ARRL.

Transport and session layers

Levels 4 and 5 of the OSI/RM also have been under development for use in amateur packet radio. A popular contender for the level 4 transport layer is *Transmission Control Protocol* (TCP). It is a complex protocol designed for dealing with inadequate or unreliable lower-layer protocols. The session layer (level 5) is also handled by TCP. For more information on TCP, I recommend *Computer Networks* by Andrew S. Tanenbaum from Prentice-Hall.

Phil Karn KA9Q has developed a *Transmission Control Protocol /Internet Protocol (TCP/IP)* program for the IBM PC. This program (NET.EXE) allows for advanced networking in amateur packet radio, although the TCP/IP system is still very experimental in nature. NET.EXE, its related programs, a file and message transfer system, and documentation can be downloaded from CompuServe's HamNet.

Presentation layer

The level 6 presentation layer has also been given some thought. The *North American Presentation Level Protocol Syntax (NAPLPS)* graphics protocol might be a means for sending graphics via packet radio. Other contenders include *File Transfer Protocol* (FTP) and *Simple Mail Transfer Program* (SMTP).

Operating amateur packet radio

Understanding how packet radio works and getting a station put together is only half the battle when first getting started in packet radio. Packet is a unique mode with its own operating characteristics. New users are usually somewhat apprehensive about operating packet because of the strange terminology and operating practices. Packet radio is simply a means of communicating information through a versatile radio channel very efficiently. As long as you keep this in mind and do not become overly concerned about the new operating procedures, you will pick them up quickly while learning to enjoy the capabilities of packet.

What you learn here will save you from "on the air" trial and error. After a while, packet becomes second nature, and new users stop thinking in terms of terminals, ASCII, RS-232, modulation methods, encoding techniques, and radios. Packet becomes a system and they realize that their station, with all its individual parts, is just a small part of a large network.

This section starts off with a discussion of user interfaces. The user interface is the first obstacle you encounter once you get your station operating. After the introduction to user interfaces, initial parameters that usually have to be set before operation are covered. Then the process of initiating conducting QSOs, and disconnecting are discussed. Bulletin board and other packet systems are covered next. Finishing up this chapter are some operating tips that might help you utilize packet radio more effectively.

The user interface

The user interface includes the command set, terminal specifications (such as screen size, baud rates, and control codes), and structure and design considerations (such as menus, modes, and prompts). Most TNCs have divided their user interfaces into three different areas, known as *modes*. Each mode serves a different purpose. The command mode is used when entering commands and changing parameters. The converse mode is used while transmitting and receiving information, and it features many editing functions for preparing your data. The transparent mode is also used while transmitting and receiving information, but it does not have any editing functions; the TNC is "transparent" to the user. The transparent mode can be used to send transmit and receive binary programs and other data that might trigger the converse mode's editing functions.

The user interface will be your window to the packet world, so you should spend some time learning about its features. The ideal user interface should be easy to use, learn, and understand. In addition, it should be flexible enough to allow the user to skip over areas that aren't of interest while simultaneously providing extensive capabilities in other areas.

Current packet user interfaces come very close to the ideal; much thought and experimentation have gone into their design. There are 2 main classifications of user interfaces: universal TNCs and specific TNCs.

A *universal TNC* is a TNC designed for use with a wide variety of terminal configurations (i.e., it works with almost any terminal). As a result, the user interfaces of universal TNCs are rather generic in design. They do not exploit the features of any one type of terminal in an effort to ensure a wide degree of compatibility.

There is little or no menu utilization, and the displays are usually very simple. They feature full command sets and 1 to 3 different operating modes. Prompts usually consist of a single line, and displays are not formatted in any special manner.

On a *specific TNC*, the user interface is adapted for use with a specific terminal (or computer). It often takes advantage of any special features that the terminal may have, such as graphics capability and function keys. Because the screen size and other variables are known, menus and complex displays are often used. A full command set is offered, but because of the structured design of the interface, certain commands can be accessed only in certain sections. For example, transmitter parameters can be accessed only from the radio interface menu.

The command set includes all commands and other parameters that can be utilized by the user. There are 2 types of commands: those that are executed immediately and then forgotten, and parameters that are altered and retained for future reference. For example, the connect command is executed and must be reentered when you want to connect to another station. But the retry command is a parameter that is set by the user and is recalled each time a frame is set.

The TAPR command set is the most prevalent in packet radio today, and has been widely copied in the majority of TNCs. It is the standard in much the same way as the Hayes command set has become the standard in the land-line modem world. (Some other command sets have been developed for use with particular TNCs, such as the WA8DED code for the TNC-1 and compatibles, and the GLB command set).

The major benefits of the TAPR command set are that it is easy to learn and use. It features a full English syntax along with optional abbreviations (Fig. 6-17). For example, the command to connect to KR3T is Connect KR3T, or it can be abbreviated to just C KR3T. The TAPR command set has 3 modes: the command mode, the converse mode, and the transparent mode.

In the command mode, most commands are followed by an argument. For example, in the Connect KR3T example, Connect is the command and KR3T is the argument. There are 2 types of arguments: toggle and response. A toggle argument

```
TAPR packet radio
RAM length is 2000
cmd: display id
BEACON      EVERY 0
BTEXT       TAPR/AMSAT AX.25 level 2 protocol software
version 3.3
CWID        OFF
IDTEXT
MYCALL      KR3T
MYVADR      $11
UNPROTO     CQ
cmd:
```

Fig. 6-17. The TAPR user interface. The display command is used to display parameters. In this case, only the station's ID parameters were selected.

switches between 2 different conditions. The toggle argument in the TAPR command set consists of "On" or "Off." The second type of argument, response, consists of a string of characters as in Connect KR3T, in which Connect is the command and KR3T is the response string or argument. After typing a command and argument, a key (usually RETURN or ENTER) must be pressed. This lets the TNC know that the command is finished and ready to be processed. If an error has been made when the command was entered, the TNC displays an error indicator and redisplays the command prompt.

Initial parameters

Several commands must be set to configure the TNC so that it will work properly with the rest of the stations. These commands can be divided into 3 categories: terminal parameters, radio parameters, and operational parameters. *Terminal parameters* are those commands that must be set to the proper values necessary for communications with the terminal. *Radio parameters* are those commands that must be set to the proper values necessary for interfacing with the radio. *Operational parameters* are those commands that must be set to the proper values for specific operating conditions.

This section lists the commands that usually must be configured before going on the air. Not all TNCs have all the commands listed, and many have more. However, this section gives you an idea of what parameters need to be set, and specific references are made to the TAPR and GLB command sets. In most TNCs, once a parameter is set it is permanently retained so that it is not necessary to reconfigure the station each time the TNC is turned off. Some even retain more than one set of parameters so it is easier to configure the TNC for different operating conditions such as HF, VHF, and satellite.

Terminal parameters   Some of the terminal parameters deal with configuring the RS-232 serial link between the terminal and the TNC. (Refer to appendix D for more information on the RS-232-C interface.)

The first terminal parameter is the *baud rate*, the rate of data transfer between the TNC and terminal. In this case, the baud rate is equal to the number of *bits per second (BPS)*. Do not confuse the terminal baud rate with that of the radio link. The terminal baud rate on most TNCs is capable of running at up to 19,200 BPS. The terminal baud rate should be set to that of your terminal. The default value is usually 300 baud on most TNCs.

Some TNCs have an autobaud routine, which monitors the output of the terminal and automatically adjusts to match it. Once the terminal baud rate is set, the TNC must be reset before it will communicate at the new rate. The TAPR command for the terminal baud rate is ABAUD.

The next terminal parameter is the word length. This is the number of bits per character. It is set to either 7 or 8 for ASCII and 5 for Baudot. Most ASCII terminals only recognize 7 bits unless told otherwise. Eight bits allow for special characters not included in the regular 128 ASCII character set. The default is usually 7 bits per word. The TAPR command for the terminal word length is AWLEN.

Another terminal parameter is the number of stop bits to follow each character, either 1 or 2 bits. With an 8-bit word length, only 1 stop bit is usually allowed. The default is usually 1. The TAPR command for the number of stop bits is ABIT.

The final serial interface terminal parameter is the type of *parity* desired. Parity is a form of error detection that counts the number of bits in a character and sets an additional bit, called the parity bit. There are 2 types of parity: even and odd. In even parity, if the number of 1 bits in a character is even, the parity bit will be set to 0; if off, it will be set to 1. In odd parity, the opposite is true—if the number of 1 bits is odd, the parity bit will be set to 0; if even the parity bit will be set to 1.

It is also possible to ignore parity by setting the parity parameter to "none" or "off." If no parity is requested, the TNC should not even include a parity bit in the transmission. However, in some cases, the parity bit may be set continuously at either 0 or 1 and simply not checked. The TAPR command for setting the type of parity desired is PARITY.

If the default TNC parameters do not match those required by your terminal, simply type the appropriate command and the desired argument in the command mode and it will be changed. In most cases, it is best to start out with a 1,200-baud terminal baud rate, a 7-bit word, a 1-bit stop bit, and even parity. Be sure your terminal parameters are set to the same values as the TNC. If your terminal doesn't seem to be working, try experimenting with different parameters.

Machine-specific TNCs and software TNCs usually do not use an asynchronous serial port for terminal-to-TNC communications, so they will probably not have these terminals commands.

The following TNC parameters can be classified as terminal characteristics. These commands configure the output from the TNC to your terminal.

Screen width   The first of these parameters is the *screen width*. This is the number of characters the TNC will send before adding a line-feed character. Set this to the character width of your display device. The TAPR command for setting the screen width is SCREEN. The default is usually 80 characters per line. Even if your display is not 80 characters, you might want to leave the screen length set to 80 so that printouts of received text are properly formatted, since most people use 80-column display devices.

Nulls   The next parameter controls the number of nulls sent after each line feed or carriage return. This allows time for the terminal to get ready for the next line. A *null* is a blank character that causes the terminal to do nothing. Most CRT terminals do not require any nulls. However, in the case of hard-copy terminals, nulls might be required after each carriage return to allow time for the mechanism to return the printhead to the beginning of the next line. A slow CRT terminal might require nulls after a line feed to allow time for the terminal to update the video display.

In the TAPR command set, the command to activate the sending of nulls is NULLS (ON/OFF); NULLS is a toggle command. The Commands NUCR and NULF are used to set the number of nulls to be sent after a carriage return character and line-feed character, respectively.

Echo   With the echo parameter, it is possible to configure the TNC to echo characters received from the terminal back to the terminal for display. Note that this is not the same as echoing characters to a printer from a terminal. If the terminal is set for full-duplex operation and the TNC is set to echo, all characters typed are sent back to the terminal for display. However, if the TNC is set to echo and the terminal is set for half duplex, both the terminal and the TNC send the character to the display and double characters will result. Either enable the echo feature and set the terminal to full duplex or disable the echo feature and set the terminal for half duplex. It is usually better to set the TNC to echo so you can be sure that the characters are being received properly. The TAPR command to set the echo is ECHO.

Auto line feed   Another terminal parameter is the auto line feed. If this is set, the TNC adds line-feed character after each carriage return sent to the terminal. If the terminal also adds a line feed after a carriage return, double spacing results. The TAPR command to add a line feed is AUTOFL.

Casing   If your terminal does not support lowercase characters or if you wish to use casing to differentiate between sent and received text on the display, the TNC can be configured to send only uppercase characters to the terminal. All lowercase characters received by the TNC are converted to uppercase before being sent to the terminal. The TAPR command is LCOK.

Control codes   The remainder of the terminal parameters deal with control codes. These are special characters recognized and acted on by the TNC. Most are for editing in the converse mode. The default values usually work fine with most terminals.

The first control code is the backspace character. This is one of the most frequently used characters, since it is used to remove typing mistakes. It can be used in both the command and converse mode. There are actually two keys that can be used for correcting typing mistakes: the backspace key and the delete key. The backspace key is represented on most terminals as the left arrow or BKSP. The delete key is represented (on the keyboards that have one) by DEL or DELETE. The TAPR command to choose between these two keys is DELETE. DELETE is a toggle command and ON selects the delete key; OFF selects the backspace key.

A hardcopy terminal obviously can't backspace over characters that have already been printed, so the TAPR command set allows for corrections on hardcopy terminals using a different method. The TNC can be configured to send a "/" to the terminal for each character deleted. On a CRT terminal, the TNC backs the cursor one space, displays a space, then backs the cursor again. To select between the two methods of updating the display, the TAPR command BKONDEL is used. If BKO DEL is ON, the CRT updating method will be used. For a hardcopy terminal with a backspace key, DELETE should be OFF and BKONDEL OFF.

Other heavily used control codes are the Xon/Xoff flow control codes, used to temporarily interrupt the data flow using Xon/Xoff software flow control. The control characters to be used can be set. The values should be set to those of the terminal. The default is Xon/Xoff enabled, the Stop character set to CTRL-S, and the Start character set to CTRL-Q. The TAPR command to toggle between Xon/Xoff enabled and disabled is XFLOW. The control characters are set with the START and STOP commands. The GLB command set does not include Xon/Xoff commands.

The commands to set the control character to exit the converse or chat mode and return to the command mode is COMMAND, for the TAPR command set. The default for COMMAND is CTRL-C.

Terminal commands   The following terminal commands are used in the converse and chat modes to edit data being typed in for transmission.

The TAPR CANPAC command is used to delete the data entered since the last packet sent. The default value for CANPAC is CTRL-Y (HEX 19).

The TAPR CANLINE command is used to delete the data inputted since the last carriage return (CR) was typed. The default value is CTRL-X (HEX 18).

The TAPR REDISPLA command is used to set the control code used to redisplay the current line being inputted. The default value is CTRL-R (HEX 12).

The TAPR SENDPAC command is used to set the character used to send a frame. The information entered since the last SENDPAC is put into a frame and transmitted. The default is a carriage return <CR>1 (Hex 0D). Whenever a <CR> is pressed, a frame is sent.

Radio parameters   The next group of TNC parameters deals with the radio. They are designed to tell the TNC about the timing characteristics of the radio and the network to which it is interfaced.

The most important radio parameter is the transmitter delay. This parameter tells the TNC how long to wait after keying the transmitter before sending the frame. This time is required by the radio to key up properly. In the TAPR command set, TX DELAY is the command used to set the delay. A number within a certain range is entered. That number is then multiplied by a time value to give the total delay.

The TAPR command set allows for an additional delay period for use with slow audio repeaters or receivers with a slow squelch release. This delay is the time to wait in addition to TXDELAY before sending data. The command is AXDELAY and the argument follows the same guidelines as TXDELAY.

There is one more TAPR command used in conjunction with AXDELAY which is used to negate the AXDELAY. This is necessary when using an audio repeater with a long squelch tail (meaning the repeater remains keyed up for a time period after repeating). Since the repeater is already keyed up, there is no need to wait AXDELAY before transmitting. If the TNC has heard a packet within a time period, it will not add AXDELAY to the TXDELAY. This time period is set by the AXHANG command. It uses the same arguments as AXDELAY.

Machine-specific TNCs and software TNCs also have radio parameters, since they do not contain integrated radios.

Operational parameters   The last section of commands are the operational parameters. These commands are used to set the TNC to match your operating preferences and local operating conditions.

The first command is used to select the protocol you wish to use when operating. On older TNCs, the selection is between AX.25 and VADCG (V-1). On current TNCs, the selection is between AX.25 Version 1 and AX.25 Version 2. The TAPR (TNC-1 version) command to select between AX.25 and V-1 is AX25. AX25 uses a toggle argument with ON selecting AX.25 and OFF-selecting V-1. The TAPR (TNC-2 version) command to select between AX.25 V1 and AX.25 is AX25L2V2. This is a toggle command also with ON selecting Version 2.

The next command is used to select which of the communications modes is entered upon establishing a connection. The choice is between converse and transparent; converse is almost always chosen. The TAPR command to select which mode is to be used is CONMODE. The two arguments are CONVERS and TRANS; CONVERS is the default value.

The TAPR command CONOK is used to indicate if your station is available for connection. CONOK is toggle command with ON selecting connection availability. If CONOK is set at OFF, the originating station will receive a busy message. The CONOK default is ON.

The next command is similar to CONOK but is for use in allowing other stations to use your station as a digipeater. If your station is available for use as a digipeater, the command should be enabled. In the TAPR command set, there are two digipeater commands: one for AX.25 and one for VADCG (V-1). The TAPR (TNC-1 version) commands are DIGIPEAT (ON/OFF) for AX.25 and VDIGIPEA (ON/OFF) for V-1. Only one TNC in a particular area should be activated as a V-1 digipeater. Check with other local operators before you activate the VDIGIPEA command.

The TAPR command FLOW controls the flow of received data from the TNC to the terminal. The received data can be sent to the terminal immediately upon reception, or it can be held if the user is in the process of typing a line until the carriage return key is pressed. This command works in both the command and converse modes. This command keeps the screen clearer but takes away the advantage of rapid interaction between users. The TAPR command is FLOW (ON/OFF) with the default ON limiting the flow of received data, as described previously.

The TAPR (TNC-1 version) command HBAUD is used to set the *link baud rate*, the baud rate of information sent to and received from the modem. Remember that Bell 202 is 1,200 baud and Bell 103 is 300 baud. The TAPR command HBAUD is set according to a table of values. The default is 1,200 baud.

The next four commands are used to enter your station's address. In AX.25, the address of your station consists of your callsign plus a substation ID number between 0 and 15. In VADCG (V-1) the address consists of a number between 0 and 31. Some TNCs contain the user addresses in ROM, so it may not be necessary to enter yours. The TAPR command to enter your AX.25 address is MYCALL. The TAPR (TNC-1 version) command to enter your VADCG address is MYVADR. Newer TNCs may contain a second AX.25 address when using the TNC as a digipeater. This second address may be set to an area code, airport identifier or anything else (it must be 6 characters or less).

The TAPR command XMITOK can be used to disable the TNC from transmitting. It is useful if the station is left on and unattended for long periods of time to prevent someone from accidentally keying the transmitter. XMITOK is a toggle command and the default is ON meaning it is OK to transmit.

The remaining TNC commands are used to configure the timing and other specifics of the TNC, and it will probably not be necessary to change them from their default values until you have a solid working knowledge of the networking conditions in your area.

The DWAIT command is used to reduce congestion on the channel by allowing digipeated packets first chance at the channel. Thus the digipeated packets are less likely to be collided with and then will not have to be sent all over again from the originating station. All stations except digipeaters have to wait the time period set with DWAIT before transmitting. A digipeater that is ready to transmit at the same time as a user will capture the channel first. The DWAIT command is set in small time intervals. The DWAIT should be set to a little over the TXDELAY of most transmitters (i.e., DWAIT = 100 to 200 ms).

The RETRY command sets the number of times a frame is to be retransmitted before unilaterally disconnecting. The TNC sends a frame a total of this value plus 1 since the first transmission was not a retransmission. For example, if you want only 15 attempts at sending a frame before disconnecting, the value should be 14. The TAPR command is RETRY and the default is 10. A 0 means unlimited retries.

The next command, FRACK, sets the length of the wait after sending a frame before it is retransmitted if no acknowledgment is received. If the path of the connection includes digipeaters, it takes longer for the frame to reach the destination station and for the acknowledgment to return than if the two stations were linked directly. As a result, the total delay is adjusted for each digipeater. The formula for determining the total delay is FRACK*(2*# of digis) + 1. Thus, if there are no digipeaters in the path, the total delay equals the FRACK value. In the TAPR command set, the FRACK value is set in increments of 1 second.

The MAXFRAME command sets the maximum number of frames that can be transmitted at a single time. There is an upper limit of 7 under AX.25. If some of the frames in a transmission are acknowledged, they are dropped and that many more added to the next transmission if they are available.

The last command sets the maximum number of bytes (or characters) of user data that can be included in a frame. When the keyboard input reaches this amount, the user data is automatically put into a frame and sent. The TAPR command PACLEN can range from 1 to 256 bytes. The default is 128 bytes. Having more than 128 bytes of information is an extension of the AX.25 and V-1 protocols, so values greater than 128 might not work with all TNCs.

Together with the maximum number of frames command, it is possible to control the amount of data in each transmission. The maximum amount of data is 7 frames with 256 bytes of user data in each. Short transmissions are more likely to get through without error in conditions of interference or congestion as found on HF. Long transmissions are more efficient on reliable, open channels.

By now you know what packet radio is, how it works, how to set up a station, and how to configure the TNC. The next step is to actually get on the air and operate amateur packet radio.

Monitoring

One feature available on all TNCs that is very useful when first getting on the air, as well as for regular operating, is monitoring. Monitoring allows you to monitor activity on a channel by disassembling all frames received by your station that meet certain conditions you specify. In other words, you can select the activity you want to monitor. The general TAPR command for monitoring is MONITOR. It is usually a toggle command with ON selecting monitoring. However, other TNCs may implement a numeric response code for an argument that selects the type of monitoring desired. It is usually possible to monitor selectively only frames containing user information, control frames, digipeated frames, or frames with specified addresses.

The first connection you should attempt is to yourself through a digipeater. This process allows you to check your station and get used to the process of initiating a connect, transferring information, and disconnecting. But before you can connect to yourself, you need to locate a digipeater that you are able to use. Digipeaters are usually easily located by monitoring. Look for a frame sent as unnumbered information to a general address such as "BEACON," which states that the station is available for use as a digipeater. Some digipeaters might not advertise their availability, so monitor the activity of other stations in your area.

Beacons   Now is a good time to introduce the subject of beacons. A *beacon* is a frame sent as unnumbered information. An unnumbered information frame is sent (broadcast) on the channel for all users to receive. It can be sent regardless of whether the TNC is connected to another station. Because there is no destination address, a user-selected dummy address is placed in the address field of the frame. The dummy address is usually BEACON, although CQ is sometimes used.

In the TAPR command set, the text to be sent in a beacon is entered using the BTEXT command. Beacons can be sent periodically or only after activity is heard on the channel. The command to activate the sending of a beacon is BEACON. The argument for a beacon to be sent repeatedly every specified time period is EVERY # (# = number of time intervals). The argument for a beacon to be sent after a specified pause in activity is AFTER #. The TAPR command to set the dummy address used by the beacon is UNPROTO and can include up to 8 digipeaters.

Unnumbered frames also can be broadcasted manually by entering the converse mode with the CONVERSE command and inputting the text. This method can be used when you want to transmit information to a number of users at a single time, such as in a roundtable discussion. However, there is no guarantee that the frames will be received correctly by all stations since there is no error-checking. When the send packet character is pressed, the frame will be broadcast using UNPROTO as the destination address.

Just because all TNCs have the capability to send beacons does not mean that they should be used by all users. Beacons should be reserved for information that is of importance to a large number of operators. They should always be kept as short as possible, and the time period between transmissions should be kept as large as possible.

Connecting to your terminal   Once you have located a digipeater by monitoring or other means, you should try to connect to yourself through it. All commands are generic TAPR because of its popularity. The command to connect to another station through a digipeater is CONNECT call VIA digi. Up to 8 digipeaters can be used and are separated by commas. For example, suppose I want to connect to myself using KR3T-1 as a digipeater. I type CONNECT KR3T VIA KR3T-1 at the command prompt; the abbreviated form is C KR3T V KR3T-1.

My TNC transmits a connect request frame, which is received by KR3T-1 if it is in range and operating. KR3T-1 sees that its address is in the digipeater field and resends the connect request. My station, KR3T, receives the connect request and sends an acknowledgment to KR3T, which is digipeated by KR3T-1. Once I receive the acknowledgment, I am connected to myself and automatically put in the CON MODE, usually converse.

Anything I send is sent back to me by KR3T-1 (Fig. 6-18). Typing a CTRL-C puts

```
cmd:c kr3t v kr3t-1
cmd:*** CONNECTED to KR3T
I am connected to myself using KR3T-1 as a digipeater
I am connected to myself using KR3T-1 as a digipeater
Everything I send is digipeated back to me
Everything I send is digipeated back to me
Notice the connect command on the top line and the
***CONNECTED to message
Notice the connect command on the top line and the
***CONNECTED to message
cmd:d
cmd:*** DISCONNECTED
cmd:
```

Fig. 6-18. Example of a self-connection using a digipeater.

me back in the command mode where I type DISCONNECT. After the disconnect request is sent via the same path as the connect request and acknowledged, I am disconnected from myself.

More information on connecting through digipeaters is given later in the chapter.

Connecting to another station   Now that you are sure the station is operating properly because you were able to connect to yourself, you can connect to another packet station and conduct a packet QSO. The first example shows how to connect to another station without the use of a digipeater, and the second demonstrates the use of multiple digipeaters.

Make sure your station is properly set up (correct frequency, your call entered, CONOK ON, and XMITOK ON). Look for the CMD: prompt. If it is not visible, press the <CR> key, and if that doesn't work, type COMMAND character (usually CTRL-C) or the Xon START character (usually CTRL-Q). As a last resort, turn the TNC off and on again. Pick a station to connect to that is within range of your station, possibly one that you have monitored recently.

The following example assumes you are trying to connect to my station, KR3T-1.

Type C KR3T-1 at the CMD: prompt, which means send a connect request frame to KR3T-1. Then press the <CR> or RETURN key. The transmitter should key up briefly as the connect request is transmitted.

There are 3 possible outcomes to a connect request. The first is that you will *retry out*. This means that your TNC retransmitted the connect request RETRY number of times without receiving a response. When this situation occurs, the station you are attempting to connect is out of range or not operating properly. The retry message will look like this: ***Retry count exceeded. (Fig. 6-19.) You are then unilaterally disconnected and returned to the CMD: prompt.

```
cmd:connect kr3t-1
cmd:*** retry count exceeded
*** DISCONNECTED
cmd:
```

Fig. 6-19. The "retry out" message.

The second possible outcome is that you receive a busy message from the station you tried to connect to. This looks like ***KR3T-1 busy (Fig. 6-20.) This message indicates that I am already connected to another station or that I have my CONOK command turned OFF.

The third possible response is that I acknowledge your connect request, and we will be connected. We are each sent a ***Connected to Call message (you see my

```
cmd:connect kr3t-1
cmd:*** KR3T-1 busy
*** DISCONNECTED
cmd:
```

Fig. 6-20. The "busy" message.

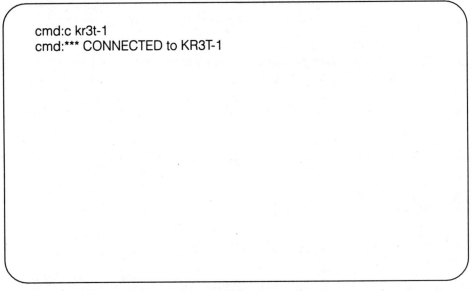

Fig. 6-21. *The connected message at KR3T.*

call and I see your call) and put in the converse mode by our TNCs, assuming that is what we have each set our CONMODE to. (Figs. 6-21 and 6-22.) Now everything that we type on our terminals is put into frames and sent to the other station. The TNC keeps sending the frames until it receives an ACK from the other station. If no ACK is received and the frames have been retransmitted RETRY number of times, the sending station retries out.

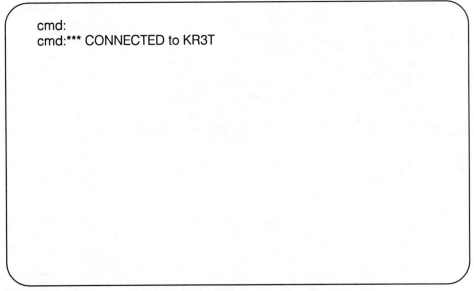

Fig. 6-22. *The connected message at KR3T-1.*

```
cmd:
cmd:*** CONNECTED to KR3T
Hello KR3T-1. Equipment here is a TRS-80 Model IV
with a TAPR TNC-1 and an IC-271A.>>
```

Fig. 6-23. Received frames from KR3T.

The frames received by each TNC are disassembled and the information portion sent to the terminal (Figs. 6-23 through 6-25.) It is possible to return to the command mode during a QSO and alter or check parameters and initiate commands by typing the COMMAND character (usually a CTRL-C). The CMD: prompt is then displayed. When you are through and want to return to the QSO, type CONVERSE at the CMD: prompt, and the TNC switches to the converse mode again.

```
cmd:
cmd:*** CONNECTED to KR3T
Hello KR3T-1. Equipment here is a TRS-80 Model IV
with a TAPR TNC-1 and an IC-271A.>>
Good afternoon KR3T.  Thanks for the connect.
Equipment on this end is an IBM/PC-XT interfaced to
a Pac-Comm TNC-200.  Radio is an IC-02AT with amp.>>
```

Fig. 6-24. Additional text to KR3T.

```
cmd:c kr3t-1
cmd:*** CONNECTED to KR3T-1
Hello KR3T-1. Equipment here is a TRS-80 Model IV
with a TAPR TNC-1 and an IC-271A.>>
Good afternoon KR3T.  Thanks for the connect.
Equipment on this end is an IBM/PC-XT interfaced to
a Pac-Comm TNC-200.  Radio is an IC-02AT with amp.>>
```

Fig. 6-25. Text sent to and received from KR3T-1.

When you are through with the QSO (Figs. 6-26 and 6-27.), either station may initiate a disconnect by returning to the command mode and typing DISCONNECT (abbreviated DISC or just D) at the CMD: prompt. A disconnect request is sent to the other station and if acknowledged, the stations are each disconnected. If the other TNC does not acknowledge the disconnect request, it is retransmitted up to RETRY a number of times. You are then unilaterally disconnected. It is also possible

```
cmd:c kr3t-1
cmd:*** CONNECTED to KR3T-1
Hello KR3T-1. Equipment here is a TRS-80 Model IV
with a TAPR TNC-1 and an IC-271A.>>
Good afternoon KR3T.  Thanks for the connect.
Equipment on this end is an IBM/PC-XT interfaced to
a Pac-Comm TNC-200.  Radio is an IC-02AT with amp.>>
FB.  Well, TNX for the quick chat.  I have to run.
U Disc.  73>>
```

Fig. 6-26. Additional text to KR3T-1.

```
cmd:
cmd:*** CONNECTED to KR3T
Hello KR3T-1. Equipment here is a TRS-80 Model IV
with a TAPR TNC-1 and an IC-271A.>>
Good afternoon KR3T.  Thanks for the connect.
Equipment on this end is an IBM/PC-XT interfaced to
a Pac-Comm TNC-200.  Radio is an IC-02AT with amp.>>
FB.  Well, TNX for the quick chat.  I have to run.
U Disc.  73>>
```

Fig. 6-27. Additional received text from KR3T.

for you to initiate a unilateral disconnect by typing the DISCONNECT command a second time at the CMD: prompt; however, unilateral disconnections are not good operating practice.

When you are disconnected from another station the TNC sends a ***Discon-nected message to your terminal. (Figs. 6-28 and 6-29.) You are now able to connect to another station.

```
cmd:
cmd:*** CONNECTED to KR3T
Hello KR3T-1. Equipment here is a TRS-80 Model IV
with a TAPR TNC-1 and an IC-271A.>>
Good afternoon KR3T.  Thanks for the connect.
Equipment on this end is an IBM/PC-XT interfaced to
a Pac-Comm TNC-200.  Radio is an IC-02AT with amp.>>
FB.  Well, TNX for the quick chat.  I have to run.
U Disc.  73>>
Roger.  Will try to connect with you later.  73
cmd:d
cmd:*** DISCONNECTED
cmd:
```

Fig. 6-28. Disconnect initiated by KR3T-1 and acknowledged by KR3T.

```
cmd:c kr3t-1
cmd:*** CONNECTED to KR3T-1
Hello KR3T-1. Equipment here is a TRS-80 Model IV
with a TAPR TNC-1 and an IC-271A.>>
Good afternoon KR3T.  Thanks for the connect.
Equipment on this end is an IBM/PC-XT interfaced to
a Pac-Comm TNC-200.  Radio is an IC-02AT with amp.>>
FB.  Well, TNX for the quick chat.  I have to run.
U Disc.  73>>
Roger.  Will try to connect with you later.  73
*** DISCONNECTED
```

Fig. 6-29. KR3T is also disconnected.

Some TNCs allow a user to be connected to more than one station at a time. Each connection is assigned a logical channel (or stream), and the user can switch between QSOs by selecting the proper channel. The ability to connect to more than one station simultaneously is known as *multiconnect capability.*

Connecting through digipeaters   If the station you wish to connect to is out of range of your station, you can use digipeaters to bridge the gap between the two stations. The TAPR extension of AX.25 lets up to 8 digipeaters be used. The addresses of all digipeaters to be used must be known beforehand. To initiate a connect through digipeaters type C Call V Call, Call, . . ., Call (i.e., C KR3T V AA3F, KR3T-1). The connect request will be received by AA3F, digipeated to KR3T-1, and then digipeated to KR3T. Packets from KR3T will be sent to KR3T-1, to AA3F, and finally to your station. The remainder of the QSO is identical to that of a direct connection.

In order to use digipeaters effectively it is necessary to learn a little about how they work. Most TNCs are capable of performing digipeater functions. A digipeater is a simplex packet relay station that receives all frames and checks to see if its address is contained in the digipeater address field. If the digipeater finds its address and it is its turn to relay the frame, the digipeater updates the digipeater address field to the next digipeater, if any, and then immediately retransmits the frame if the channel is clear.

Digipeaters do not retain copies of digipeated frames in memory or look for an ACK from the next station. The ACK for the digipeated frame must come from the destination station and be digipeated back to the originating station. Thus, if a frame is lost while being digipeated, the originating station must retransmit the frame from the beginning. This type of acknowledgment is known as an *end-to-end ACK.*

Digipeaters have many drawbacks. They are useful and beneficial to packet radio as long as they are used properly and responsibly. One user misusing digipeaters can cause heavy congestion on a channel. Each digipeater used increases the amount of channel time a frame consumes and the range of the transmission. The more times a frame is digipeated, the higher the chances that it will be lost along the way as the result of a collision or interference. The probability of getting a frame to its destination error-free on the first attempt is reduced geometrically as the number of digipeaters is increased.

Only use as many digipeaters as are absolutely necessary to maintain the link to the other station. Most active areas have several strong digipeaters that will allow you to reach most other local users in 1 or 2 hops. However, do not use more than 2 or 3 digipeaters on a moderately congested channel, and try to avoid digipeaters at all if the channel is very busy.

There are special digipeaters that are capable of receiving on one frequency and transmitting on another. These digipeaters are known as *dual-port digipeaters*; the ports are on different frequencies. The dual-port digipeater can be used as a regular digipeater by receiving and transmitting frames on a single port. The advantage of a dual-port digipeater lies in its ability to automatically route frames that are received on one port or the other.

When a frame is received for digipeating, the next callsign in the address field is examined. If the callsign is recognized by the dual-port digipeater as being on the other frequency, the frame is routed out on the other port. Alternately, if the dual-port digipeater does not recognize the callsign, it examines the callsign's SSID. Based on a prearranged SSID-based system, the frame is routed out the appropriate port. This system allows traffic to be switched off the user's channel and digipeated on another, less-used frequency.

The maximum of 8 digipeaters was added to allow remote areas to communicate over long distances. However, because of the rapid growth of packet radio it is almost impossible to use anywhere near 8 digipeaters anymore in a moderately active area. Digipeaters are an admitted kludge to allow for rudimentary networking until the development of true level-3 network nodes. The use of digipeaters for long-range communications will drop off significantly once these network nodes are implemented.

More operating tips are given at the end of this chapter. Now we will turn our attention to one of the largest areas of amateur packet radio activity: bulletin board operation.

BBS operating

Bulletin boards are known by a variety of nomenclatures, including BBS for Bulletin Board Station, PBBS for Packet BBS or Public BBS, CBBS for Computerized BBS, and Mailbox. Bulletin boards open a new realm in amateur packet radio by providing non-real-time operations. It is possible for 2 users to access a BBS at different times and still transfer information.

All bulletin boards provide some form of message storage. A user may connect to the board and send a message to be stored in the board's memory or storage. Another user may then connect to the BBS later and read the message. Once a message is stored on a BBS, it usually can be read an unlimited number of times. Thus, bulletin boards are an excellent method for sending messages to a large number of users.

Packet bulletin boards have existed almost as long as packet radio itself. And like amateur packet radio, bulletin boards have gained many new features and applications over the years. The current packet bulletin boards offer a wide variety of services for their users that greatly extend the usefulness of packet radio.

Just as the TAPR TNCs have become the *de facto* standard for design and user interfaces, one bulletin board system has emerged as the standard in amateur packet radio. This BBS system was developed by Hank Oredson W0RLI and is in use worldwide.

The first W0RLI BBS went on the air in February 1984 in Massachusetts and has been spreading ever since. Oredson's first BBS was modeled after an electronic message system that he had developed while working for Sperry Corporation. The system has been heavily modified over the years by Oredson in response to comments and suggestions by users.

The original W0RLI BBS ran on an IMSAI system but was ported over to a Xerox 820 CP/M machine in March 1984. The basic W0RLI configuration consists of a Xerox 820 computer board with keyboard, monitor, one or two disk drives, and one or two TNCs with radios. The W0RLI system has been under constant development since it was first brought out in 1984. Starting at Version 2.0, it has progressed into a final form at Version 11.6. Although Oredson expects to continue making minor revisions, he is finished with all hard-core modifications at this time.

The W0RLI system has been ported to many other computer systems besides the Xerox 820 with a high degree of compatibility. These W0RLI clones include an IBM-PC version written in Pascal by WA7MBL, a Commodore 64 version by WB4APR (not completely compatible), an OS-9 version by VE3FXI, a DEC Rainbow version written in Pascal by AK1A, and a version for the DEC PDP-11 by KA1T. Versions of the W0RLI system have also been written for the TRS-80 Model 100 and Kaypro computers.

This section describes the W0RLI BBS in detail and gives examples of commands and operating procedures.

The W0RLI BBS system features a message system whereby messages can be stored on the BBS for retrieval by other users or forwarded to other BBSs. There are files available for downloading, such as general information (for example, user lists and newsletters) and computer programs. There is a provision available on many W0RLI BBSs for linking to other frequencies through the BBS; these are known as *gateways*. A frequency activity monitor and message beacon, which lists those stations who have messages waiting for them on the BBS, are also included.

To use a W0RLI BBS, just connect to the station as if it is a regular user station. Digipeaters are fine although some BBS owners (known as SYSOPs for system operators) have imposed a limit on the number of digipeaters that may be used. The SYSOP's callsign is usually the address of the BBS.

A short time after your station receives the connect acknowledgment from the BBS station, an opening message appears. The opening message usually gives the station's call, the SYSOP's name, and the station's location. At the end of the opening message, a prompt appears that usually includes your call, the date and time, and sometimes an abbreviated list of available commands. The prompt always ends with a > sign.

There are many commands available to control the BBS. All commands are composed of a single letter, although many can be expanded further by the addition of another delimiter character, which restricts the range of the command. The commands can be broken down into groups by the BBS function they control.

Mail system The first group of commands covered is used to interact with the message (or mail) system, since it is the most heavily used part of the BBS. Messages are sent to specified users by callsign. The user's call is automatically entered as the originating, or FROM, station. A BBS station to forward the message to can be specified.

In the early days of the W0RLI system, the number of packet users was low enough that it was feasible to keep track of where each user was located and which BBS he usually used. Thus mail addressed to that user would be forwarded to that BBS. However, with the growing number of users logging onto the systems, it is not possible to keep track of where all the users are located. Thus, some of the forwarding responsibility has been transferred to the users by requiring them to include the address of the BBS station the recipient uses if it is not the same as the one at which the message originated.

The first mail command most new users like to try is L(IST). The L command instructs the BBS to send the user a listing of all the new messages added since he last logged onto the system. The format of the listing is as follows: message number, message status, message size, 2TO call, FROM call, BBS call, date sent, and message title (Fig. 6-30).

Msg#	TR	Size	To	From	@ BBS	Date	Title
125	Y	136	K3XXX	KBXXX		860509	Listings msgs
124	Y	165	K3XXX	KA2XXX		860509	TNC for sale
120	Y	241	K3XXX	KB3XX		860507	monitor for sale
119	N	254	W3XXX	KB3XX		860507	Need help
116	N	389	ALL	W3XXX		860507	HAMFEST

Fig. 6-30. A sample message listing as would be received from a W0RLI-compatible BBS.

All messages are numbered sequentially, and that number is the message number. The message status indicates the message type and whether it has been read by the recipient. There are several types of messages, including bulletins, private messages, ARRL messages, and traffic.

Bulletins are messages meant to be read by all who log onto the system. They include items for sale, upcoming events, system changes, and other news. Bulletins are indicated by message type B. Private messages are meant to be read only by the sender and recipient. They do not show up on a message listing to anyone other than the sender, the recipient, and the SYSOP; however, when sending or receiving private messages, they may be monitored by other users. Private messages are indicated by a message type P. ARRL bulletins and messages are indicated by a message type A. Traffic includes any messages meant to be forwarded by the *National Traffic System (NTS)*. They are indicated by message type T and are usually read by a local traffic operator and then entered into the traffic net on some other mode, since packet is not yet fully utilized by the NTS. Regular messages may be listed and read by all users. The message type for regular messages is left blank.

The indicator as to whether the message has been read by the intended recipient shows an N if it has not been read by the intended recipient and a Y if it has. The indicator does not change if someone other than the intended recipient has read the message.

The message size consists of a number indicating the length of the message in bytes. If a message is very long (2,500 bytes or more) it might be better to read it later if the channel is crowded or someone else is waiting to use the BBS. The FROM call is usually the same as that of the user who sent the message; however, if the message was forwarded to another BBS, the FROM call shows the call of the BBS that last forwarded the message.

The TO call indicates the callsign of the intended recipient of the message. The TO call never changes regardless of forwarding. The BBS call is the callsign of the W0RLI-compatible BBS to which the message is to be forwarded. The date gives the date that the message was stored on the BBS; if the date has changed when a message is forwarded, the new date is shown. The message title is entered by the user who sent the message. The title may change if the message is forwarded to indicate that it was.

The L command also accepts several delimiters and arguments to allow users to list messages selectively. As mentioned earlier, sending the BBS a single L at the prompt results in a listing of all messages stored on the BBS (except private messages that are not from or to the user) since the user last logged on. The addition of a B after the L restricts the listing to all the bulletin type messages stored on the system (i.e., LB—List Bulletins). By typing an M, rather than a B after the L, the system will list all the messages either sent by or for him (i.e., LM—List Mine).

The remainder of the list commands require the addition of an argument after the 1- or 2-letter command. The addition of a second L, a space, and a number (LL 4), causes the system to send a listing of the last specified number messages (except private messages not to or from the user), starting at the latest message and working backwards. For example, the command LL 5 (List Last 5) causes the BBS to send a list of 5 messages, starting with the last message number and ending with the last message number minus 5.

The L command, a space, and a message number causes the BBS to send a listing of all messages stored on the BBS starting with the message number specified up to the last message number (L 1000). The L command with a < character, a space, and a callsign causes the BBS to send a listing of all messages from the specified callsign (i.e., L< KR3T); the private message restriction applies here and in the following examples also. The L with a > character, a space, and a callsign causes the BBS to send a listing of all messages addressed to the specified callsign (i.e., L> KR3T). The L command with an @ character, a space, and a BBS callsign causes the BBS to send a listing of all messages with the specified BBS callsign entered by the sender for forwarding (L@ W0RLI).

The 8 list commands just given are very useful, and being familiar with them can help reduce the time needed to find a particular message out of the several hundred normally stored on a BBS. Note that the command and delimiter are not separated by a space and that a space is required after the command (and optional delimiter) before an argument.

The next mail command to be discussed is the read command. The read command, R, is used to read messages. There are only two forms of the R command R # and RM. The R, a space, and a message number causes the BBS to send the entire text of the specified message number. It is not possible to read a private message not to or from the user or a message that does not exist. If this is attempted, the BBS responds with an appropriate message and redisplays the prompt. The RM command stands for Read Mine and causes the BBS to send the user the full text of all his messages that have not yet been read.

The third mail command discussed is the send command. The send command, S, is used to instruct the BBS to store a message. There are several versions of the send command. The first method is to send the BBS an S, which causes the BBS to prompt for the destination callsign and the message title. Once these are sent, the message can be transmitted. Once the message has been sent, a CTRL-Z is used to indicate that the message is over. The system then saves the message to disk, adds it to the message list, and redisplays the prompt.

An easier method is to include the addresses and optional BBS call with the S command (S KR3T or S KR3T @ WA3XXX). The BBS does not ask for the destination callsign if this method is used. The S command can include delimiters to indicate the type of the message (i.e., SP = Spend Private, SB = Send Bulletin).

The fourth and last mail command, K, kills a message. The K command must have a message number as an argument (i.e., K 1203). If a K command is sent and the user's call is in the TO or FROM field, the message is deleted. However, if the user's call is not in the TO or FROM field of the message indicated by the message number argument, the message is not deleted, and a message informing the user that he cannot kill the message is sent by the BBS followed by the prompt. The K command followed by the M delimiter instructs the BBS to delete all messages addressed to the user (KM = Kill Mine). It is considered good practice to kill a message after it has been received if it is not of general interest.

File system   The next group of commands deals with the file system, which allows users to upload and download various files from the BBS. A file can consist of a list of local hamfests, a computer program, the minutes from the last packet meeting, a list of new packet operators, and almost anything else that can be represented in ASCII characters. Files are stored in a separate section of the BBS from messages. However, the commands are somewhat similar.

All files are stored on disk drives on the BBS computer. Each file is assigned a name when it is stored on the BBS. This name is referred to as the *filename*. If you are familiar with computers, you know that filename syntaxes vary from one system to another. The filenames for a TRS-80 operating under TRSDOs differ from those for an Apple under ProDOS. The filename syntax is controlled by the type of disk operating system the computer is utilizing. As you may recall from chapter 1, the *disk operating system (DOS)* handles all accesses by the computer to information stored on the disk drives.

The W0RLI BBS program runs under the CP/M operating system and uses the same filename syntax as standard CP/M systems. In CP/M each disk drive is assigned an alphabetical designator ("A" for the first drive, "B" for the second, and so on). The individual files on a particular disk are stored on the disk's directory. Thus, obtaining a listing of the files stored on a disk is called getting a directory.

The filenames, under CP/M are composed of up to 8 characters, a period, and a 3-character extension (for example, HAMFESTS.MAY). The filename usually describes the contents of the file.

An analogy can be drawn between a multidrawer file cabinet and the file structure on a BBS. Just as a file cabinet's drawers each contain different file folders, each disk contains different files. On each file folder in a drawer is written a short, descriptive heading describing the contents of the file folder. Each disk contains a list of short, descriptive headings (filenames) describing the contents of the file. Finally, in the file folder is the actual file; just as the actual file is stored on the disk. Each drawer has a limited capacity; only so many sheets of paper can be put in a single drawer. On a disk, there is also limited capacity for information storage.

To locate and retrieve a file in a file cabinet, the drawer and filename must be known. If they are not known, it is possible to locate a particular file by looking at a list of each file folder in a particular drawer. The same can be done on a disk with the directory. What a directory actually does is access each drive and list the filenames of all the files stored on the disk in the drive; the size of each file and the total amount of storage space left on the disk is also usually given.

The W0RLI command to get a directory of the files stored on the BBS is W (for What's available). The W command alone causes the BBS to get a directory of each disk and send a list of the files on each disk, along with their sizes, to the user. The total amount of space consumed and the total amount of space remaining on each disk are also sent. It is also possible to get a directory of a specified drive. Supposing a BBS has 3 drives available for files labeled A, B, and C; a user could request a directory for each of the drives individually by sending the BBS the command WA: WB:, and WC: respectively.

It is also possible to get a limited directory through the use of *wildcard characters*. A wildcard character is a special character that is recognized by the BBS in place of one of the components of the filename. The wildcard in CP/M is an asterisk (*). For example, suppose a BBS keeps an updated list of activities in various monthly files. All the files have the extension of the current month; however, the first eight characters or less before the period differ. To get a directory of all the updated files for the month of May, the user sends the BBS the command W*.MAY. Thus, all files with the extension of MAY are listed.

Now that the files stored on the BBS are known, it is time to download a file. The command to download a file from the BBS to the user's station is D followed by a space and the filename (D HAMFESTS.MAY). The drive designator may be optionally included (D A:HAMFESTS.MAY); however, the BBS will search all drives for the specified file automatically. The download consists of straight ASCII text with no error-checking beyond that which is provided by packet itself. The wildcard character may be used here also, but be careful not to download too many files at once.

It is also possible to upload files to the BBS. The command to upload a file from a user's station to the BBS is U followed by a space, the drive designator, and the filename with extension. Be sure to select a filename not currently in use. One other very important point is to make sure the disk has enough space to save the file with room to spare. It is possible to disable (crash) the BBS if a file upload is attempted without adequate disk storage space.

Once the BBS receives the command, it prompts for uploading to begin. After you finish sending a file, input a CTRL-Z to close the file.

There is no kill command for files; only the SYSOP may delete files. The range of files available for downloading is great. The ARRL *Gateway* newsletter and the W5YI report are common files, along with local maps that when printed out give a rough map of digipeaters, BBSs, and users in a specified area. Other files commonly available are listings of hamfest dates, tutorial files for new users, equipment modification instructions, computer programs, and lists of local users.

Gateway system   The next BBS area we'll discuss is gateway operations. A BBS gateway is usually a BBS with two TNCs. Each TNC is connected to a radio operating on a different frequency, often on another band. A user accessing the BBS on one frequency and TNC can instruct the BBS to forward his or her transmissions to the other TNC and transmit on the other frequency.

The command to access the gateway functions on a BBS is G. When the BBS receives the G command, it presents the user with a new gateway prompt. The commands available on the gateway prompt are C, R, U and X. C is the command used to initiate a connection through the other TNC. The C command is followed by a space and a callsign. It is very similar to the TAPR connect command. When the C command and argument are received by the BBS when in the gateway prompt, the BBS instructs the other TNC to send a connect request to the specified callsign. The U command is used to send unnumbered information frames through the other TNC. It allows the user to broadcast data from his station, through the BBS, and onto the other frequency. The R command is used to return to the regular BBS prompt.

The X command is used to obtain an extended menu, which lists all the commands available along with brief explanations. The long menu can be changed back to the short prompt by sending the X command a second line. The BBS usually uses the short prompt upon connection. New users may be more comfortable using the long menu for the first few BBS sessions, but it should not take long to learn the commands.

Other commands   The remainder of the BBS commands are discussed here.

The J command lists all the stations heard by or connected to the BBS, along with the times that their transmissions were received. This information can be useful for monitoring activity or meeting new users. The T command is used to page the SYSOP by ringing a bell at the BBS. If the SYSOP is nearby, he or she will turn off the BBS, and QSO with the user directly.

The N command is used to tell the BBS your name (N Jon). The BBS then knows your name for customized prompts.

The H command calls up a somewhat lengthy help file, which explains the general rules of the BBS. The I command causes the BBS to send a brief information file describing the equipment used at the BBS.

The last command used during a BBS session is the B command. B means Bye, and indicates to the BBS that the user is through using the system, causing the BBS to disconnect automatically and ready itself for the next connection.

There are some additional messages that the BBS may send during a session with a user. These include error messages ***What or ***I don't understand when the user sends an improper command, ***K3XXX just tried to connect when another station attempts to connect to the BBS while the user is connected, and ***Standby, the Sysop wants to chat with you when the SYSOP is switching from the BBS mode to the direct QSO mode. These messages are configurable by the SYSOP, so they vary from system to system. The BBS also sends beacons containing the calls of the stations with new mail waiting for them.

Net/ROM operations

In February 1987, amateur packet operators were first introduced to a new networking system known as NET/ROM, which has since become very popular around the country. This section provides information on the operational aspects of NET/ROM. NET/ROM was developed by Ron Raikes WA8DED, and Mike Busch W6IXU, and is sold through their company, Software 2000.

NET/ROM, contained on a ROM chip that simply replaces the regular ROM chip in any TNC-2 compatible TNC, turns the TNC into a NET/ROM network node. Users can connect to other NET/ROM nodes, as well as conventional stations, with the benefit of point-to-point acknowledgments through the NET/ROM nodes. Each node maintains routing tables to other NET/ROM nodes, so it is not necessary to specify a path between nodes.

To use a NET/ROM node, just connect to it like a regular station. NET/ROM nodes are usually known by their alias as well as the station's callsign, and the alias is often a geographical or airport designator. You can connect using designation. To locate a NET/ROM node in your area, ask other local packet operators or just monitor the local 2-meter operating frequency(ies).

Once you have connected to a NET/ROM node, you can obtain a listing of other NET/ROM nodes that the node can connect to by sending the NODES command. Simply type NODES and press the RETURN key. A list of other NET/ROM nodes will be displayed. If a node has an alias, it will be displayed immediately before the node's callsign.

You can now link up to any of the displayed nodes by using the CONNECT command. The NET/ROM CONNECT command is not the same as the TAPR user interface's CONNECT command. Keep in mind that you are already connected to a local NET/ROM node. You are simply sending a command to that node. For example, if one of the displayed NET/ROM nodes was W6IXU-1, you would type CONNECT W6IXU-1 and press the RETURN key. Your local NET/ROM node that you first connected to will now receive a message indicating that you are connected to W6IXU-1. If successful, you will receive a message indicating that you are connected to W6IXU-1. You can now use the NODES command again to see which NET/ROM nodes W6IXU-1 can link to.

Eventually, you will want to connect with an individual packet station or bulletin board. To do so, you use the CONNECT command again, only this time substitute the callsign or alias of the station with which you wish to connect. In most areas of the country, it is futile to link through more than 3 NET/ROM nodes. Keep in mind that there may be several digipeaters between each node, so your actual path might be quite extensive.

Operating tips

At times, operating packet radio can be confusing to the beginner. With all the technical details of establishing and maintaining a connection, some of the more routine tasks such as actually conducting a QSO can be overlooked. Also, there are many things that the beginning operator can do unknowingly to increase the congestion on a channel. The following operating tips are things that I have learned, along with comments from the many experienced operators with whom I have spoken.

The first tip seems obvious: don't send, or cause to be sent, any long files during times of heavy usage. This only results in tying up the frequency from other users. It is much better to switch to a less-congested channel, if one is available, or wait until the channel activity has decreased to an acceptable level. Early morning and midday are general periods of low activity.

Keep in mind what was said about digipeaters earlier in this chapter. Use as few as possible to reach your destination. Again, if there is heavy channel activity, refrain operating, or switch to another less-used channel.

If you should connect to another user and get no immediate response, it is possible that he or she just didn't notice your connection. Try sending a few CTRL-Gs, which will cause terminals so equipped to ring a bell or buzz a buzzer. Some areas discourage this practice because the terminals of stations monitoring your transmissions or the digipeaters you are using also might ring. If that does not arouse the operator's attention, leave a message with your call, the path, and the time and date (KR3T via KR3T-1 at 14:00 12 JUL 85); don't forget to disconnect from his station. This way the operator will know who connected, when the connection took place, and how to link back to you (assuming the station is dumping connections to a printer or receive buffer).

Beacons are another area of concern. Use them as little as possible. Beacons should be as short as possible and carry only necessary information. In some areas of the United States, there are so many beacons being transmitted that they are colliding with each other (automatic channel congestion)!

A large amount of the packet activity centers around BBSs. When you first connect to a BBS, leave the SYSOP a message with your name, location, and packet equipment. Most SYSOPs are interested in knowing who is using their systems, and they are good people to know.

When sending commands to a BBS, do not repeat the command if nothing happens immediately. This is difficult for many RTTY operators because they assume the first transmissions was lost. However, on packet, the command will get through or the user will retry out and be disconnected.

It is a good idea not to stay connected to a BBS for a long time during prime time. Also, do not download a large file if there is moderate activity on the channel. Before you connect to a BBS for the first time, make sure you have a reliable link by connecting to yourself through it (KR3T = me, KR3T-3 = BBS. C KR3T V KR3T-3). Otherwise, you may time out the BBS.

A time out on a BBS is different from a time out on an FM repeater. If the BBS does not hear from your station for a period of time (usually four minutes), you are disconnected. What usually happens is the link to the BBS fails and your station retries out and disconnects. Meanwhile, the BBS is still sending you frames until it retries out or waits for four minutes for your next command.

When operating HF packet, tuning is crucial. Because packet transmissions are short, it can be difficult to tune them in. A tuning indicator is a great help in this area. Also, HF packet is not nearly as fast as VHF because of the lower baud rate used and the problems with interference and propagation associated with HF operation.

I hope these suggestions make it easier for you to operate packet radio. Most packet operators are very understanding of mistakes and are more than willing to help out newcomers. Most of these suggestions have had to do with conserving frequency space because, at present, most of the packet operation is done on 1 or 2 frequencies using digipeaters. Once backbone links on other frequencies or true level-3 network nodes develop, the problems with channel congestion will not be as serious and detrimental to packet activity. Even with the present congestion problems, packet is a wonderful mode to operate, and with the future developments already being worked on by many amateurs worldwide, it will become even better.

Conclusion

This chapter has run the full course, from networking and protocols to setting initial parameters to connecting to bulletin board systems. If you have an interest in learning more about networking and protocols, take a look at a few of the networking books listed in the bibliography. If you have had some difficulty understanding the more technical concepts presented here, do not despair. In-depth knowledge of networking and protocols is not a prerequisite to operating and enjoying packet radio.

It is my hope that having some prior knowledge of the techniques used in operating packet radio will take away some of the nervousness and concern from operating packet and replace it with understanding and excitement. If things don't seem to be going right at first, relax, sit down, and think about exactly what you are doing. Most new users quickly adapt to packet radio, and it rapidly becomes one of their favorite modes.

7

Digital imaging

ONE OF THE EXCITING FRONTIERS BEING PIONEERED WITH THE LATEST ADVANCEMENTS in amateur radio digital communications technology is the world of digital image communications. Traditionally, amateur image communications modes have been based on analog transmission and reception systems. However, the increasing complexity and sophistication of today's digital technology (especially evident in digital signal processing) is opening the door to fully digital image communications systems.

Today's digital image systems are designed to be compatible with the traditional analog-based image modes such as slow scan Television (SSTV) and facsimile (fax), so the primary emphasis in this chapter is on the traditional analog modes. As the technology develops, however, we may see new image modes that fully exploit the capabilities of the digital medium.

Much as the development of solid state RTTY systems helped increase the popularity of that mode by eliminating the noisy, mechanically complex equipment previously in use, a similar increase in popularity of image modes should result as digital image systems proliferate. With solid-state image communication systems, operating image modes becomes no more complicated than operating packet or AMTOR. The ease and convenience of having a multimode digital communications interface with the standard text modes (RTTY, AMTOR, packet, etc.) along with fax and SSTV will do much to encourage operators to give image communications a try.

Image modes

Three main image communication modes are presently in use today in amateur radio: fast scan TV (FSTV), SSTV, and fax. In the following sections, each of these modes is examined with the intent of giving you an overview of the capabilities of each mode.

FSTV

Fast scan TV, also known as ATV (for amateur TV), is fully compatible with standard broadcast television. Each video frame consists of 525 horizontal lines with 30 frames transmitted each second. Thus, ATV operators can use standard video cameras, VCR, and monitors in their ATV operations without modification. Also, just like standard broadcast television, an ATV signal occupies about 6 MHz of bandwidth. Because of the huge amount of frequency space required for an ATV signal, the FCC has restricted ATV operation to frequencies above 420 MHz (most ATV operation occurs on 420 to 440 MHz and 1,240 to 1,294 MHz). Images received via ATV look much like standard television, with full-motion video and sound.

SSTV

Slow scan TV was developed in the late 1950s in an effort to transmit television images over the HF bands. SSTV is designed to send images using only 3 kHz of bandwidth. While ATV is directly compatible with standard broadcast television, SSTV is not. SSTV requires 8 seconds to transmit a single image, vs. 30 images per second in ATV, and each SSTV image is composed of only 120 lines, vs. 525 lines in ATV.

An SSTV image is transmitted using frequency modulation, varying between 2,300 Hz for white elements and 1,500 Hz for black elements. The synchronization pulses are sent at 1,200 Hz. The specifics of SSTV transmission are shown in Fig. 7-1.

Frame time	08 seconds
Lines per frame	120
Duration of line	67 ms
Duration of horizontal sync	05 ms
Duration of vertical sync	30 ms
Sync frequency	1200 Hz
White frequency	2300 Hz
Black frequency	1500 Hz

Fig. 7-1. SSTV standards.

Because SSTV uses such different transmission characteristics than standard broadcast television, standard television accessories such as VCRs, cameras, and monitors will not work directly with SSTV. Most present SSTV operators use a *scan converter*, which stores SSTV images in memory and outputs them to other devices after converting them to mimic standard broadcast TV signals. Thus, with a scan converter, an SSTV operator can use standard television accessories in his or her station.

Fax

Facsimile is a method of transmitting visual images, such as photographs and weather maps, over radio. Fax has been in use longer than any other electronics image communications system—since the late 1920s. Since then, many different fax standards have been developed to keep pace with advancing technology and changing needs. Fax images range in resolution from 800 to several thousand lines. To transmit these resolutions, fax images take from 3 to 15 minutes to send.

The image to be transmitted using fax is scanned, line by line, and converted to audio frequency signals. Fax is sent using an 800 Hz shift, with the audio signals between 1,500 Hz and 2,300 Hz. A 1,500 Hz signal represents black, and a 2,300 Hz signal represents white. Signals between the two extremes represent varying shades of gray. Fax is used by a variety of news organizations and weather services to transmit photographs and maps. Almost all fax activity is on HF outside of the amateur bands, so a general-coverage receiver is a necessity.

Traditionally, fax images were received using electrostatic or photosensitive paper wrapped around a drum. The speed at which the drum rotates is given in revolutions per minute. The drum rate determines the speed at which an image is sent.

The scanning density is another variable in fax. It is measured in lines per inch and determines how close together each received line is placed. The scan density is used to maintain the proper aspect ratio so that one inch horizontally in the received images matches one inch vertically. If the scan density is off, a received image might appear compressed or stretched. The specifics for several standard fax services are shown in Fig. 7-2.

Type of service	Size	Drum speed	Density
WEFAX/Satellite	11 in	240 line/min	75 line/in
APT/Satellite	11	240	166
Weather Charts	19	120	96
Wirephotos	11	90 or 180	96 or 166

Fig. 7-2. Fax standards.

Digital implementations

Despite the fact that using multimode digital communications interfaces for image communications is a relatively new concept, a wide variety of options are available today. Also, as advances are made in digital signal processing (DSP) technology over the next few years, we will see multimode interfaces with very advanced capabilities.

One of the pioneering multimode interfaces was AEA's PK-232. The PK-232 was one of the first digital controllers to offer image communications in the form of fax. The PK-232 uses an Epson-graphics compatible printer to produce received fax images. Any signal above 1,700 Hz (the center frequency of the PK-232's 1,000 Hz filter) causes the printer to print a black dot, and any signal below 1,700 Hz causes the printer to leave a blank. Thus, the PK-232 cannot display shades of gray that might be found in photographs. However, Weather fax (WEFAX APT) maps are transmitted using only black and white, so excellent reproduction is possible using the PK-232.

Other controllers offer additional features. The MFJ 1278 offers multigray-scale fax and SSTV operation. The AEA DSP 2232 also features multigray-scale fax and SSTV operations, as does the L.L. Grace DSP-12. Additionally, there are several low-cost interfaces designed for use with image modes. The AEA fax system allows for the reception of multigray-scale fax images. MFJ's Color fax is a simple fax, RTTY, and CW interface that features not only multigray-scale fax reception, but also reception of color fax images.

Thus far, I've been conveniently overlooking digital implementations of FSTV. Because of the extremely high throughput of an ATV signal, the processing power required to digitally receive an ATV signal is prohibitive. However, advances in DSP, along with generational advances in solid-state technology, will provide the necessary processing power at an economical level at some point in the near future. The research and development going into high-definition TV (HDTV) and the increasing use of multimedia applications in the microcomputer arena will only help to advance the level of technology.

Operation

Operating image modes is new to most digital operators, so be sure to allow extra time to acclimate yourself to the terminology and capabilities of the modes. I'm convinced it's always best to start off by monitoring other stations for awhile to gain confidence in and familiarity with your equipment. To this end, be sure to read your equipment's manual very carefully. Although a unit might advertise fax capability, it might be capable of receiving only at certain speeds. Make sure you don't find this out after wasting an afternoon trying to receive an incompatible signal.

Although many interfaces are capable of receiving an image directly to a printer, I'd suggest purchasing the appropriate software for your microcomputer that will allow you to display images on the monitor. Not only does this method save paper and allow you to make adjustments more easily, but today's graphics standards are very good and allow for excellent display of received images. Plus, many fax and SSTV software packages will allow you to save received images to disk for later viewing, printing, or even retransmission.

Since each interface is unique in its user interface, capabilities, and interfacing requirements, it is not possible for me to cover operational specifics here. The background information provided in this chapter should help you to better understand your user's manual, and between the two, you should find getting started in digital image communications a little easier.

Conclusion

Getting started in digital image communications can be intimidating. As a result, many users of multimode digital interfaces are reluctant to try out the fax and/or SSTV capabilities of their unit. This chapter was designed to provide some background information about the various digital modes so that you will be better able to understand the specific operating instructions for your interface.

Image communications can be very enjoyable, and I encourage you to give it a try. Your multimode interface can serve as a gateway to many new and interesting ways of communicating with other amateurs. Hopefully, this chapter will inspire you to give image communications a try.

8

Setting up a digital communications station

LET'S TAKE A BREAK FROM THE MORE TECHNICAL ASPECTS OF DIGITAL COMMUNICATIONS to discuss something that all users, from novice to expert, have to do to join in on the fun of digital communications: set up a station. You have already been introduced to the necessary components in the earlier chapters, so in this chapter, take a look at multimode controllers, TNCs, terminals, modems, and radios from an operational and pragmatic, not technical, perspective. Several examples of digital communications stations are given, along with suggestions to help you maximize your station's capabilities based on your particular situation. Station arrangement, RFI protection, antennas, power requirements, and portable operation are also discussed.

Obviously, everyone has a different set of objectives when setting up a digital communications station. For some, digital modes take a backseat to other methods of communication. Others see packet, RTTY, or AMTOR as their primary mode. Some want to operate HF, while others prefer VHF operation. There is no ideal station for everyone, so my advice to you is to read through this chapter and make note of anything you feel might be of use when setting up or modifying your station.

The first major decision that must be made when assembling a packet station is which terminal and digital communications controller to use. They are listed together because they must work together and be fully compatible. The next section describes several types of terminals and lists their features so you can compare them and see which is best for you.

In some cases, the terminal and digital interface are combined into a single unit. This is often true of machine-specific TNCs (TNCs designed to work with only certain computers or terminals) and software-based TNCs where a limited number of computer systems are supported. Although this arrangement can be very convenient

113

and greatly reduces the decision making required when selecting a terminal and digital interface, keep in mind the inherent lack of options. A combination terminal/digital interface might have a predefined user interface, computer system requirements, and other nonvariable features. You usually have much more flexibility with these options when utilizing a universal digital interface and a universal terminal.

However, one great advantage that combination terminal/digital interfaces have is that they are designed to work together, the digital interface might use features peculiar to only that terminal. The user interface, if well thought out, can be enhanced by taking advantage of those features.

Selecting a terminal

Most digital interfaces are designed to communicate with a variety of terminals through a standard I/O interface, such as RS-232, TTL, or current loop. Although almost any terminal will work with present digital interfaces, many options need to be considered when selecting a terminal in order to achieve maximum flexibility from your digital communications station. Terminals come in many different configurations and understanding the features available from each can help you pick a terminal that best suits your operating style.

There are 2 main types of terminals: dedicated terminals and terminal emulators. A *dedicated terminal* is a device whose sole purpose is to convert digital codes into recognizable symbols. A *terminal emulator* is a software program that allows a computer system to act like (emulate) a dedicated terminal. In addition to the distinction between dedicated terminals and terminal emulators, terminals also can be classified as either smart or dumb. We'll look first at the difference between dedicated terminals and terminal emulators and then examine the distinctions between smart and dumb terminals.

A dedicated terminal is designed to function only as a terminal, to convert digital signals to symbols and symbols to digital signals. Almost all terminals receive digital ASCII or Baudot signals through an I/O port and display their alphabetic equivalent. Information is typed on an alphabetic keyboard, and the information's ASCII or Baudot equivalent is sent out the I/O port. These terminals are called either ASCII terminals or Baudot terminals, depending on what code they use. ASCII terminals are the most common type used in amateur radio digital communications. Other types of terminals, such as graphics terminals, are not presently used much.

A hard-copy terminal generates its output on paper using some form of printer. The most common form of hard-copy terminal is the mechanical teleprinter, but it is not recommended for serious digital communications operation because of its slow speed, maintenance requirements, and noise. Modern hard-copy terminals usually incorporate a great deal of electronics and generate their output using high-speed dot-matrix, thermal, or ink-jet printers. They lack many of the features available in video display terminals (not to mention the problem of what to do about all the paper these terminals crank out).

Video or CRT dedicated terminals are very useful devices that can have many features. Some of the terminals are as electronically complex as microcomputers.

These terminals usually feature memory, full keyboards, and ergonomic design, and offer expansion, such as printers and additional features. Video terminals are usually smart terminals.

Rather than use a dedicated terminal, most amateur radio digital operators use a terminal emulator for communicating with their digital interfaces. The terminal emulator concept is very popular for several reasons. It is cost-effective because there is no additional equipment to buy beyond the computer system, and the computer can be used for other purposes. A computer can be used for a wide variety of functions by changing software, while a dedicated terminal can be used only as a terminal.

Computer-based terminals also allow for much greater flexibility in handling the information obtained through them. With a dedicated terminal, received information can only be printed out (or with some CRT terminals, temporarily stored). With a computer-based terminal emulator, the information can be permanently saved to disk, formatted and printed with word processing software, or processed using database or spreadsheet software.

Terminal emulator software comes with a wide variety of capabilities. Some simply allow the computer to serve as a dumb terminal. Other, more complicated software allows the microcomputer to function as a sophisticated smart terminal.

Some terminal emulation software is written specifically for packet or RTTY operation. This software is usually designed for use with a specific TNC or other digital interface and contains features that enhance its use. However, it is not necessary to have a terminal program exclusively for digital operation.

Most ASCII telecommunications software packages will work fine. These are the same programs used with telephone-based modems to access remote computer systems. There are a great number of terminal programs with an equally great diversity in features and capabilities. Generally, microcomputer systems with communications capabilities have terminal software available for them.

Although terminal software can cost up to several hundred dollars, it is not necessary to spend vast sums of money. A great variety of terminal programs are available in the public domain that can be obtained at little or no cost. Often, operating system master disks include some sort of telecommunications capability, especially if the computer comes standard with an RS-232 port.

If you're not sure what kind of program is best, or where to look for one for your particular computer, check with someone who is using the same type of computer you do. If you don't know of anyone, try to locate a user's group in your area; a good place to start is where you bought your computer. Be sure to look at a few back issues of computer magazines for ideas; check to see if there is one written specifically for your computer system.

I've been using the terms *smart* and *dumb* terminals throughout the preceding section without much explanation. Let's discuss the differences between smart and dumb terminals. Keep in mind that the "terminal" can be either a dedicated terminal or a terminal emulator.

A dumb terminal has only the most basic capabilities necessary for communications. It features very simple send and receive functions, most often just displaying received characters and transmitting exactly what was typed. Dumb terminals do not support expansion, nor do they offer much flexibility for modifying the communications characteristics. A good example of a dumb dedicated terminal is a mechanical teleprinter. A dumb terminal emulator is a very simple terminal program.

A smart terminal possesses advanced capabilities to enhance communications. Smart terminals are usually dedicated CRT terminals or sophisticated terminal programs. There are many features available in smart terminals. The most useful follow.

Xon and Xoff capability is a very useful, almost mandatory, feature for packet operation. The Xoff signal, usually a CTRL-S, tells the terminal to stop sending information. An Xon signal, usually a CTRL-Q, tells the terminal to resume sending the information.

This feature allows an attached device, such as a TNC, to turn the flow of data from the terminal to the TNC on and off automatically so that the TNC is not overloaded. If the device supports Xon/Xoff then the terminal can turn the flow of data from the device on and off so the terminal is not overloaded. For example, Xon/Xoff is useful when a TNC is transmitting at a much lower baud rate than is used between the TNC and the terminal. Assume the TNC's modem is transmitting at 300 baud, and the terminal is sending the TNC data at 9,600 baud. The terminal is sending information to the TNC faster than the TNC can send it out, so the TNC buffers the information buildup in its memory. When the memory is almost full, the TNC sends the terminal an Xoff character to stop the flow of data. When the buffer space is again at an acceptable level, the TNC sends an Xon character to resume the flow of data.

Other control codes than Xon and Xoff are used heavily in digital communications to control the receiving terminal. Control codes such as clear screen, bell, and linefeed are commonly used in digital communications. A smart terminal should allow for changing or filtering of control codes. For example, while many control codes are standardized (i.e., Linefeed = CTRL-J and Bell = CTRL-G), many are not. One terminal's clear screen might be another's delete transmit buffer. One of my terminal programs uses CTRL-Z as the clear screen command, which also happens to be the W0RLI Mailbox's end-of-file character. As a result, whenever I received an end of file while monitoring the mailbox, my screen would go blank. When I filtered out the CTRL-Z character before it was processed by the terminal program, the screen would no longer clear when I received a CTRL-Z from the mailbox.

The ability to download a file is extremely useful in all digital communications because it provides the ability to save incoming data for later viewing or processing. On an electronic dedicated terminal, the data is usually saved in volatile memory. On a computer system with a terminal emulator, the data can be put in volatile memory and then saved on disk. The computer has the distinct advantage in this area because of its long-term storage and processing capabilities.

Terminals differ on downloading procedure, but most allow the user to open a buffer with a special keyboard sequence and close the buffer with another sequence after the desired data has been received. The buffer then can be cleared, displayed, printed, or—with a computer and certain dedicated terminals—saved to disk. These functions can be handled through special commands or through menus. A nice feature to have in a terminal emulator is the ability to turn menus off once you have gotten used to the structure and commands, thus using direct commands, rather than having to scroll through pages of menus.

Uploading is another useful feature that smart terminals offer. Uploading allows for the sending of prepared data. The data can be saved on disk or in memory. In most systems, you specify which file or buffer is to be sent and the data is sent automatically. This feature saves time and allows the same information to be sent to multiple destinations with a minimum of effort.

Echoing allows data to be sent to another device at the same time it is being sent or received by the terminal. In most cases, the other device is a printer. With echoing, you can get a hard copy of data without downloading it into memory. This feature comes in very handy when downloading a file that exceeds the available memory on dedicated terminals and nondisk computers.

Keep in mind that many terminal systems have more features than I have listed here; these are the basics that you should look for in a smart terminal for use with amateur radio digital interfaces. The dividing line between smart and dumb terminals is fixed, so more attention should be given to a system's features than its designation. Some terminals are smarter than others, but with increased capability usually comes increased complexity. The bottom line is to find a terminal that has the features you need and feel comfortable using.

My recommendation as to the first terminal you should consider is a microcomputer system with a smart terminal emulator program. This system provides maximum flexibility. You can retain information permanently, and with a CRT, you can control the amount of paper you generate. However, a computer system with disk drives, RS-232 port, and a printer (Fig. 8-1) can be expensive, although prices have dropped markedly over the past few years. Be sure to take a look at the used computer market. If necessary, you can get by without a disk drive or printer for awhile and add them later as your budget allows.

Fig. 8-1. A TRS-80 Model IV running terminal emulation software and connected to an AEA PKT-1.

If you already own a computer, then it's time to look for some good terminal software. Check the computer to see if you need to add an RS-232 port, for serial communications, or a printer port. If you already have these things, then you're all set.

If you happen to share a computer with the rest of the family and cannot afford one exclusively for amateur radio use, do not despair. You can use the computer for occasional downloading, and a cheap dumb terminal for everyday monitoring and rag-chewing. A computer is very useful in the shack, and you should seriously consider putting aside a little money toward one exclusively for amateur radio use.

If you don't have a computer and don't want one, you can use a dedicated terminal. If you decide on a hard-copy terminal, try to get one with as high a baud rate as possible. The minimum limit for moderate use is 1,200 baud. Mechanical Teletypes such as the Model 33 are just too slow for anything other than monitoring activity or infrequent operation. Also keep in mind that a hard-copy terminal cannot be used for graphics (such as fax and SSTV) display as can often be done with a computer running terminal emulation software.

Make every effort to get a terminal with an RS-232 port. Almost all amateur radio digital interfaces use it for terminal communications. Besides, with an RS-232 port, the terminal can be connected to a multitude of other devices. Try to avoid current loop if at all possible. For more information on terminal devices along with information on interfacing teleprinters, read *TV Typewriter Cookbook* by Don Lancaster from Sams.

Many inexpensive home computers, such as the Commodore 64, contain a serial I/O port. However, their I/O ports use TTL levels and are not usually compatible with RS-232 levels. Thus, it is necessary to convert the port to RS-232 levels (which is fairly easy to do) or to select a digital interface unit that is compatible with TTL levels.

Current loop is another form of digital I/O that can be used with some digital interface units, although it is very uncommon to find anyone actually using current-loop systems these days. Current-loop I/O is not very convenient and performance suffers, but it is possible. Current-loop systems usually are associated with the mechanical teleprinters of yesteryear, which were very common in RTTY systems before the advent of affordable solid-state systems. Current-loop systems are still available, usually at very low prices, if you are charged anything at all.

Since most digital interfaces utilize RS-232 compatible I/O, an RS-232-to-current-loop must be attached to the digital interface. The digital interface is then put into the loop, along with the teleprinter and paper tape devices. Flow control is a common problem experienced when adapting an RS-232 device to a current loop system.

If you are not interested in having a complete current loop, but simply want to use the teleprinter as a terminal for a TNC or other digital interface, you can connect the TNC directly to the teleprinter. You also can build a special interface to convert the RS-232 level signals to current pulses, which trigger the teleprinter. Alternately, if an RS-232 interface is available for the teleprinter, one can be installed and the TNC wired directly to it.

Selecting a digital interface

When you are selecting a digital interface, most commonly a TNC or multimode unit, several items should be considered. The command set, or user interface, controls your access to the interface. Command sets vary from full-English commands to short, sometimes cryptic, abbreviations. The advantage of an English syntax is the ease of remembering the commands. Abbreviations have the advantage of being faster to type once you have grown used to them.

The TAPR command set has become the industry standard and most present-day TNCs and multimode units use a similar command set.

The TAPR command set allows users to type the full command or an abbreviation, for example Connect or C. In some cases, more than 1 or 2 characters need to be typed to distinguish between similar commands, for example MYC for MYCALL and MYV for MYVADCG.

Another area of possible concern when selecting a digital interface is power consumption, especially if you are planning portable operation. One way to lower the power consumption of some TNCs is to replace the NMOS chips with their less power hungry CMOS equivalents, if they're available. Some TNC manufacturers offer low-power TNCs designed especially for portable operation.

The digital interface's buffer size can be important if you are using a slow terminal or doing extensive off-line monitoring. A slow terminal causes information to back up in the interface, and sufficient buffer size is necessary to hold the data until the terminal is ready to receive it. If the terminal is disconnected or otherwise taken offline, the digital interface can buffer received information until the terminal is back online. The amount of memory that comes with most digital interfaces is more than adequate in most cases. If you find that it is not, additional memory sometimes can be added.

The digital interface is the most important piece of equipment in the digital communications station; thus, it is a good idea to select your digital interface first and arrange your station around it. Only compromise on the digital interface if digital operations are not among your primary modes of communication.

The modem is usually built into the digital interface. If it's not, check the manufacturer's recommendation. Select the correct modem type for the band of operation. Some characteristics to look for in a modem for general-purpose digital operations are a fast carrier detect and a non-PLL demodulator for HF operation. Status indicators for Transmit (TX or PTT) and Data Carrier Detect (DCD) are helpful. Be sure to check the interfacing data for connecting the digital interface to the modem, as well as connecting the modem to the radio.

Selecting a radio

A transceiver is the most convenient radio system for digital operation. The rig should meet the specifications given in the chapter on packet radio. One of the most important characteristics is the R/T and T/R times (the time it takes a rig to switch from receive to transmit and from transmit to receive). Try to get a rig with as low a value as possible for both. Once again, for VHF almost any FM transceiver will work fine. For HF, a stable SSB transceiver is required. Also, a tuning indicator for the digital interface's modem is very useful. A photograph of the radio equipment currently in use at my station is shown in Fig. 8-2.

The modem-radio interface is usually not very difficult. In most cases, there

Fig. 8-2. The radio equipment at KR3T. A Kenwood TS-430S is used on HF; an Icom 271A is used for two-meter base operation; and an IC-02AT is used for portable operation.

are just 2 cables running from the modem to the rig: the microphone cable and the phono or external speaker cable. There are usually no internal connections to the rig unless you are using squelch detect or bypassing certain sections of the rig.

Especially when operating packet, you should connect the squelch detect option when sharing a channel with voice users. The carrier sense system does a good job of keeping a TNC from transmitting on top of another packet station, but it does not do a good job of keeping a packet station from transmitting on top of phone operators. However, not all TNCs have squelch detect.

The squelch detect connects to the rig at a point where the voltage varies according to squelch conditions. Most digital interfaces that implement the feature look for a voltage that goes from under 2 V to over 3 V when a signal is received. If your rig's voltages go in the opposite direction, you might need an inverter to get the proper voltage levels for the digital interface. A good spot for tapping the voltage is the receive or busy indicator light on most rigs.

The microphone connector has 3 main connections: mic audio, PTT, and ground. The mic audio carries the AFSK from the modulator to the transmitter. The PTT trips the rig into the transmit mode. Be sure to check your rig's PTT characteristics to see if they are compatible with the modem's. The PTT line is usually a direct connection, but an interface might be required for some rigs. The ground shields the mic audio lead and should be at the same potential as the radio's ground.

The speaker connection runs to the modem's demodulator. The cable consists of an audio lead, along with a ground. There are 3 possible taps for the audio: phono jack, external speaker jack, and discriminator. The photo jack just plugs into the headphone connector on the front of most rigs. There are usually 2 positions: all the way in for no internal speaker output and part of the way in for both photo plug and speaker output.

The external speaker jack is usually located on the back of the rig, and when the plug is in, no audio goes to the internal speaker. Some digital interfaces do have an external speaker jack, which allows monitoring of the received signal. When connecting to the discriminator, you get the signal before processing and possible distortion. This is an internal connection and in most cases need only be done when distortion is suspected in later stages.

The modem connection usually consists of a single plug, although many types of plugs are used. Some modems have separate plugs for audio connections so they have individual shielding to help reduce interference. Shielded cable is recommended for all connections, although ribbon cable can be used if there is no interference. Most modem plugs are designed to accept ribbon cable connectors.

If you have many mic connections, I do not recommend using separate mic connectors. They are expensive, and constant insertion and removal will wear out the socket on the radio. The system I use is to wire a mic connector to a 5-pin DIN in-line socket. You can get away with 5 pins because the rest aren't needed for digital operation. You can use a piece of shielded cable a foot or so long to slightly lengthen the overall length of the cable.

Then wire the modem's cable to a 5-pin DIN in-line plug. Make sure the pins are wired properly. Now insert the plug into the socket and you're all set. All future connections to the same rig need only have a DIN plug. Be sure to keep all cable runs as short as possible and the mic/audio lead shielded.

Sample stations

Individual digital communications stations vary greatly from one user to another. Each user's goals, budget, and priorities are different. It should be evident by now that despite the requirements of digital communications, there is quite a bit of latitude for the individual user to customize a station to meet his or her particular needs.

In this section, several stations are presented. They include a typical station, a budget station, a station with a shared computer, a station using the current loop, and a portable station. Hopefully, you will find something useful in the examples that will aid you in setting up your own station.

Typical station

The typical digital communications station arrangement used by an overwhelming majority of operators consists of a microcomputer with terminal emulator software, an RS-232 port, and disk-based storage; a multimode digital controller, packet-only TNC, or single-mode interface; and a 2-m FM transceiver for VHF operation and a modern HF transceiver. Most of the characteristics of the components have been covered earlier, so I won't go over them again. The microcomputer can range from a Commodore 64 (Fig. 8-3) or a TRS-80 Color Computer to a TRS-80 Model IV or an Apple IIe (Fig. 8-4) to IBM-PCs and Apple Macintoshes. The terminal emulator soft-

Fig. 8-3. The Commodore 64 microcomputer.

Fig. 8-4. An Apple IIe (running terminal emulation software) connected to a Kantronics KPC-2.

Fig. 8-5. A TRS-80 Model I (running terminal emulation software) is connected to a Heathkit HD-4040. A Kantronics KPC-2 is set atop the HD-4040.

ware is usually very capable and offers a wide range of features. Most users have two or more terminal software packages that they are comfortable with.

This is the arrangement that I recommend in most cases because it is widely used, well tested, and extremely flexible (Fig. 8-5). If one component needs replacing, it can be switched without altering the other equipment. For example, if you get a new computer, you can just unplug the digital interface's RS-232 cable from the old computer and plug it into the new computer. It is also very easy to adapt the system to work with all modes, such as Baudot and ASCII RTTY, CW, packet, and AMTOR, with the appropriate multimode digital interface or additional single-mode interfaces. Also, the computer can be used for other purposes such as logging and QSLing contacts, satellite tracking, and antenna design.

The cost of this system varies greatly. A low of $575 (a $300 computer system, a $125 TNC or single-mode interface, and a $150 used transceiver) is easily realized, although used equipment might have to be considered. A high of $5,600 (a $3,000 computer system, a $400 multimode interface, a $700 VHF transceiver, and a $1,500 HF transceiver) can be obtained by selecting new, top-of-the-line equipment. Of course, it is possible to spend even more money, but I doubt you will see an appreciable benefit in operating characteristics. Keep in mind that this system is usually implemented by users who already have a computer system available.

Couple the computer system with a well-equipped station, and the only components needed are a digital interface and terminal emulation software. If you don't have a computer yet, you should, and digital operation provides an excellent excuse to get one.

Budget station

If you don't have much money to invest in digital communications, consider taking some ideas from the system I have arranged. An inexpensive system is centered around the digital communications interface. It is the most important part of the digital communications station and should receive the most consideration in a financially limited situation. The terminal and rig can be upgraded later, but with a flexible, capable digital interface, almost any hardware configuration can be made to work.

I have divided the terminals into 3 levels based on cost. The lowest level consists of a mechanical hard-copy teleprinter with an RS-232 port. Avoid this type of terminal if at all possible because its speed is slow. However, its price cannot be ignored. A mechanical hard-copy teleprinter can be had for a very low price, if you're charged anything at all. I once received a perfectly good Model 33 ASR for free by just asking for it.

The middle level consists of a high-speed hard-copy terminal. These units often have speeds in excess of 1,200 baud and usually have a full implementation of the RS-232. However, they generate a lot of paper and can be a little noisy, although those with thermal printers are usually very quiet. These terminals can be obtained at hamfests and computer shows for $50 to $100.

The high level of the budget terminal market consists of an inexpensive microcomputer or CRT terminal. An inexpensive microcomputer such as the Commodore

64 and the TRS-80 Color Computer sell for around $100 without accessories. By the time you add a cassette drive and software, the price is around $150. Don't forget that you'll also have to supply a monitor, since these computers don't come with one. Check the used market for some good deals on complete systems.

A CRT terminal usually can be found surplus for around $100 to $150. Make sure it has an RS-232 port. There is nothing wrong with using a CRT terminal for casual operation, but a computer offers you more for the money.

The digital interface is what you want to concentrate your available funds on. Check the used market. You might be surprised to find a TAPR TNC-1 or other early TNC at a great price. Older solid-state RTTY Terminal Units (TUs), such as the Kantronics Interface II or UTU, also can be found at reasonable prices. However, the best way to go, assuming you want to operate all digital modes, is with a modern multimode digital interface, such as the AEA PK-232 or Kantronics KAM. These units might cost more than comparable single-mode units, but they cost much less than the several single-mode units that would be required to match the features included in one multimode unit.

Many digital interfaces, particularly TNCs, are available in kit form. If you order a bare kit with just a PC board and EPROMs, you can build your own unit at a much reduced price—depending on how good you are at scrounging components. The complete kits are often comparable in price to their assembled and tested counterparts (within 10 to 15 percent), so you will have to judge whether the small monetary savings are worth the time and effort involved in assembly.

For the radio, just use a 2-m HT or transceiver for VHF operation. If one is not available, get a simple crystal-controlled channelized rig. Try to get a radio with as fast a T/R and R/T time as possible. For HF operations, a clean, stable rig is needed. If your digital interface doesn't have a built-in tuning indicator, an external one might be necessary.

Shared terminal

If you have access to a microcomputer near your shack but are sharing it with the rest of the family or using it as a business computer, consider the following options. If the computer is located in a room other than your shack, you can run an RS-232 cable from the digital interface in your shack to the computer. As shown in appendix D, it is not necessary to have all 25 pins connected, so you can get by with as few as 3 wires. As long as you don't need the HF rig or to rotate a beam from the shack, this system can work well. A VHF station can be set and left. You can use the computer for other tasks and then switch over to a telecommunications program when you wish to operate. An RS-232 switch might be needed to switch the computer's RS-232 port between the digital interface and other devices, such as a printer or land-line modem.

A cheap terminal can be used to monitor activity when the computer is going to be busy for awhile. A connect alert, which beeps when someone connects to your station, is a useful feature to alert you to switch over to the digital interface. Connect alarms are available for some TNCs as a built-in function or as an add-on kit.

If you are sharing the computer with non-hams, be sure to consider the possibility of their accessing the digital interface and getting on the air. It would be a good idea to disable the digital interface from transmitting (with the command XMITOK in the TAPR parlance) when not using the digital interface. This system allows you to access the digital interface from a remote location, which at first might seem to be an inconvenience, but it can be refreshing to get out of the shack and operate while sitting in the living room listening to the evening news.

Portable station

Portable operation with packet radio is very useful. It is a lot of fun and can be used while on trips or vacations. Emergency communications is an area of amateur radio that benefits greatly from the application of packet radio in the field. It is possible to fit an entire packet station with smart terminal, TNC, and radio in an attaché case with room left over (Fig. 8-6).

Fig. 8-6. A complete portable packet station in a briefcase consisting of a TRS-80 Model 100, a Pac-Comm TNC-200, an IC-02AT, and a gel cell battery.

The basic requirements for a portable packet station are that it must be truly portable, consume as little power as possible, and possess full operating capabilities. A portable computer makes an ideal portable terminal. Units such as the TRS-80 Model 100 (Fig. 8-7) feature an LCD display, full-size keyboard, built-in telecommunications software, an RS-232 port, and a printer port. All of this capability fits in a case the size of a three-ring binder and weighs about the same. The entire computer is powered by 4 AA batteries for up to 20 hours. Supplemental power supplies are also available that allow for extended operation.

The Model 100 is very popular with packet operators, because of its reputation, low price, and availability on the used market. Its built-in telecommunications software features Xon/Xoff, download and upload, echo to printer port, and high baud

Fig. 8-7. The TRS-80 Model 100 portable computer.

rates. Many optional accessories are available, including a battery-operated disk drive and printer, many software packages, and memory add-ons.

Other portable computers also are used with equal success, particularly laptop PCs, such as the Toshiba T-1000SE. Also, a battery-operated hard-copy terminal is a possibility. These units often feature built-in acoustic couplers for use with the telephone system. If the terminal has an RS-232 port, it can be connected to the TNC and used as a terminal. However, these units are usually classified as dumb terminals. The advantage of the hard-copy terminals is their extremely low price in today's used market.

The TNC should draw as little power as possible; 250 mA should be the maximum current drain considered for a battery-operated portable station. Some manufacturers offer a version of their TNC with CMOS chips, which draw much less power than their NMOS counterparts. They also generate less heat, which is especially advantageous in a crowded portable arrangement. Today, there are several TNCs available that are designed for portable operation and draw very little power.

For VHF operation, a hand-held is the most obvious choice. They are compact and battery operated, and can generate up to 5 W of power. Some require a special interface to allow the TNC to control the PTT. An amplifier can be added for additional range. However, an amplifier can increase the T/R (transmit to receive) and R/T turnaround time of the radio significantly, as well as drain copious amounts of battery power.

Any antenna system commonly used for FM phone will probably work successfully on VHF packet. Of course, when operating at a fixed location for awhile, you probably will want to put up an antenna with higher gain characteristics. I have had good luck with a regular rubber-duckie antenna running about 2 W in dense urban areas where digipeaters are readily available.

Batteries are the most obvious power supply for a portable packet station. Twelve-Vdc gel-cells, although rather heavy, offer 3 to 6 amphour ratings and can be used to power almost any station. The same power system can be used to run the TNC, radio, and computer. Also remember to bring along a battery charger.

HF operation is not very common in portable packet stations. Power requirements, size, and antenna space are the major restrictions to portable HF operation. Most of the HF rings that are used for packet operation are modern transceivers, such as the Kenwood TS-430S. However, if you do manage to set up a portable HF station, be sure to get a multimode controller so you can take advantage of the more common HF digital modes.

Although a fully operational portable HF station is prohibative, today's multimode controllers make it possible to easily monitor HF digital communications on the road. The HF portion of my portable station consists of the Radio Shack DX-440 portable shortwave receiver connected to the HF port of a Kantronics KAM multimode interface (Fig. 8-8). I often use a Heathkit active antenna to improve reception. With the DX-440 and KAM, I can monitor all forms of digital communications, such as Morse code, RTTY (both Baudot and ASCII), and AMTOR.

The entire station will fit, although somewhat cramped, into an oversized attaché case. If necessary, you could leave out the active antenna, although I wouldn't want to be without it. This station has all the advantages of a packet-only portable station, with the added benefit of being able to monitor HF digital transmissions. Of course, you also can monitor regular shortwave broadcasts.

The advantage of this setup is its flexibility. Now when I travel, I can operate local 2-m packet, copy 40-m RTTY and 20-m AMTOR, monitor the HF packet BBSs on 14.107 MHz, listen to the BBC, and set my watch to WWV.

Fig. 8-8. KR3T's latest portable station consists of a Kantronics KAM, Icom 02AT, Realistic DX-440, Heathkit Active Antenna, and TRS-80 Model 100.

RS-232

Since the RS-232 standard is used so much in digital communications, I have included an appendix (D) to cover the various peculiarities involved with interfacing equipment. If you run into problems when connecting your digital interface and terminal, check the appendix for possible solutions.

Radio frequency interference

One problem that many amateur radio operators who work with computer equipment in the shack experience is radio frequency interference (RFI). Just as computer equipment can interfere with TVs and stereos, it can interfere with amateur radio equipment. RFI can be a maddening problem, and a logical approach is necessary to identify and correct it.

Even if you haven't experienced RFI, it is a good idea to take note of all the computer equipment in your shack. Of course, your desktop micro is the best place to start, but don't forget your digital interface and any other devices that use digital circuits. You might experience RFI later on and immediately blame it on your micro, only to discover that the culprit was an easily overlooked piece of equipment, such as a digital clock.

RFI can be experienced on the HF and VHF bands. RFI is generated by computer equipment's internal signals. Computer signals are in the form of square waves, which are composed of many sine waves. Because computer signals are switched so quickly, the sine waves cover a broad bandwidth. If the computer is not well designed and lacks adequate shielding, the computer-generated RF can leak out of the computer system and invade other electronic equipment in the shack, or elsewhere in the house.

Digital interfaces are usually designed to eliminate RF interference problems because of the sensitive on-board modem section. This is not to say, however, that a digital interface should not be suspected of causing RFI. The FCC now regulates RFI levels for manufacturers of computer equipment. However, some early micros, such as the TRS-80 Model I, were not well shielded, so they generate a great deal of interference.

The FCC classifies microcomputer equipment in two grades, A and B, depending on the equipment's ability to cause RFI. A-rated equipment is the worst; this rating is given to computer equipment designed for use in office environments, where extraneous RFI is not of much concern. Class B equipment is much better. Manufacturers of Class B equipment must take additional care to minimize RFI leakage. Equipment with a Class B rating is suitable for use in homes where Class A equipment would disrupt radio and television signals. Most microcomputers are either Class A or B. Obviously, Class B is preferable for use in an amateur radio station.

If you suspect you are experiencing RFI, the first thing to do is to identify its source. Turn off each piece of computer equipment in the shack, one at a time, and listen for the interference to stop. Before you turn off a computer with a keyboard, type on it to see if you notice a change in the interference signal corresponding to your typing. If you find the trouble lies with the computer, power it up and make sure the interference returns. Try powering up one component at a time and isolate the offending component. If possible, substitute for the component to see if the fault lies with your particular unit.

If you find the interference is coming from the main CPU unit, disconnect all peripherals except for the digital interface. Check for interference again. If there is still interference, disconnect the digital interface. If the interference disappears, then it must be coming out the digital interface's cabling.

The first step for RFI reduction is to rearrange the station. Move the computer equipment to a separate electrical circuit. Check the computer equipment's case. Is it well shielded? Is is made of metal or plastic? Check the motherboard. Is it grounded? Do the CPU and related components have a metal housing around them?

If the case has inadequate shielding, try coating the inside of the case with aluminum foil or tape, copper plating, or conductive spray. If you suspect the interference is leaking through the cables, try varying the length of the cables; they might be acting as antennas. If the cable is not shielded, replace it with a shielded cable or wrap it with foil. These solutions also can help protect the computer equipment from outside interference.

RFI can be a difficult problem to solve. Always start out with easier solutions and work your way up to the more complex. Check with owners of similar equipment for possible solutions. A pamphlet available from the Government Printing Office deals with RFI: "How to Identify and Resolve Radio-TV Interference Problems," Stock No. 004-000-00345-4. You can order it from the U.S. Government Printing Office, Washington, DC, 20402. Also, contact the manufacturer of your computer equipment for information or suggestions to help you.

Antenna systems

Thus far, we have been concentrating on the most obvious parts of a digital communications station, such as terminals, digital interfaces, and radios. However, once the modulated RF has left the transmitter, there are several steps that you can take to maximize its range and quality. Your station's reception also can be improved.

In VHF operation, antenna height is always an advantage. A vertical omnidirectional antenna can be used for monitoring, and a directional antenna can be switched in when operating. This system will allow you to monitor from all directions, yet when operating, use no more power than necessary, have a directed signal, and let other stations use the frequency at the same time. A strong omnidirectional station will be received by many stations over a wide area. Depending on your local operating characteristics, it might be to your advantage to increase your range beyond the station you are communicating with if you find you are being transmitted on top of by a strong station that cannot hear you. This will enable the carrier sense of the stronger station and allow you to have uninterrupted transmissions.

A directional antenna's gain characteristics and limited field of view can help when you are receiving a weak signal. Preamps can be useful when dealing with weak signals, but beware of possible distortion. A good deal of your VHF antenna needs will depend on local conditions. How far is it to the nearest station? Is there a strong digipeater that you receive, but cannot reach?

For HF operation, no special antenna systems are usually needed. A strong signal is important to counter the interference found on most bands. On HF, it is not possible to be as selective in coverage and range as it is on VHF. A good, stable transceiver is your best plan of attack for HF operation.

Receive diversity is a concept that can be applied to both HF and VHF operation. In a receive-diversity system, two antennas are located apart and connected to the same radio through a splitter. This arrangement can help improve reception, especially on HF with changing propagation conditions. It is always a good idea to maximize the performance of the receive section, regardless of the specific methods used. A good receive section can reduce the number of retries needed because of reception errors.

Although amplifiers can increase your signal range and quality, they also can greatly increase the T/R and R/T of your radio. Also beware of possible distortion, as with any component added in the signal's path. Use of good-quality, low-loss coax is another way to reduce the loss of your station's antenna system and maximize your power output.

Chances are good that your regular antenna setup will work fine. Use it as is and adapt it to digital operation as necessary. Remember that vertical polarization is used on VHF. For more detailed information, check a book on antenna system design. Although antenna systems are an important consideration, first concentrate on the other areas of your station that require more adaptation for digital operation.

Conclusion

In this chapter, the many variables that go into setting up a digital communications station have been examined. The cost of setting up a digital communications station varies widely, depending on what equipment you already have and what kind of station you want. If you make the various choices logically with an idea of the complete system in mind, you will have few regrets.

9

Equipment
and accessories

THIS CHAPTER PROVIDES A COMPREHENSIVE OVERVIEW OF AMATEUR DIGITAL communications equipment that is currently available. Some of the equipment listed is no longer manufactured, but is included because it represents a major development in recent amateur radio digital communications. You also might run across this equipment in the used market or when talking with other operators. For these reasons, it is a good idea to have a knowledge of the various products in use today.

Previews of products currently under development were provided by various manufacturers. They are included in this chapter to give you an idea of what to expect in the future. If you are interested in an item, be sure to check with the manufacturer as to the progress of that product's development.

This chapter includes all types of amateur radio digital communications interface units, TNCs, software, and hardware additions. The products are listed in alphabetical order by manufacturer, group, or individual; the addresses are included in appendix F. Any pricing information given is subject to change.

AEA
DSP-1232/2232

AEA has announced two DSP products: the DSP-1232 and DSP-2232 (Fig. 9-1). The DSP-1232 and DSP-2232 are similar products: the DSP-1232 has two switchable radio ports, while the DSP-2232 has two simultaneous radio ports. The modem sections are both capable of operating all standard HF digital modes, standard VHF packet, HAPN's 4,800 bps standard, K9NG's 9,600 bps standard, AEA's 2,400 bps standard,

131

Fig. 9-1. The AEA DSP-2232.

and all Microsat and OSCAR modem standards, as well as WEFAX and SSTV. New modem standards can be added by a firmware update.

The AEA units operate like the AEA PK-232, with a similar command structure and user interface. The DSP-2232 can operate as a gateway with its simultaneous radio ports, and also features a two-line LCD display. The DSP-1232 can be upgraded to include DSP-2232 features. The DSP-1232 will list for $798.00, and the DSP-2232 will list for $999.95.

PK-232

The AEA PK-232 is a very popular multimode data controller (Fig. 9-2). It is capable of operating on CW, Baudot RTTY, ASCII RTTY, AMTOR, packet, and facsimile. The PK-232 has 21 front-panel indicators. Two radio ports allow for the simultaneous interfacing of an HF and a VHF transceiver. The list price of the PK-232 is $319.95.

AEA also sells two terminal programs for use with the PK-232. PC Pakratt with fax is for the IBM PC and compatibles. Comm Pakratt with fax is a ROM cartridge for the Commodore 64 and 128. Both programs have a split-screen display and can transmit and receive facsimile.

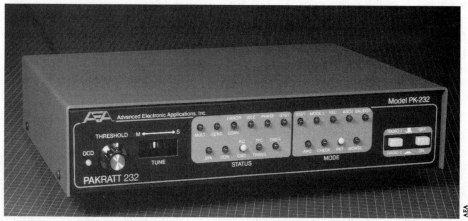

Fig. 9-2. The AEA PK-232.

PK-88

The PK-88 is a standard TNC-2-like TNC (Fig. 9-3). It features a "maildrop" through which others can exchange information. The PK-88 is compatible with the TCP/IP protocol and can be modified for NET/ROM operation. It lists for $119.95.

Fig. 9-3. The AEA PK-88.

PM-1

The AEA PM-1 (Packet Modem) is designed to interface between your existing TNC and radio (Fig. 9-4). The PM-1 contains independent dual-channel filtering for maximum sensitivity and selectivity under poor HF conditions. It is optimized for 300-baud operation; a frequency shift of 200 Hz or 600 Hz can be selected from the front panel. A bar tuning indicator is provided to assist with precise tuning. List price is $199.95.

RFM-220 Radio Modem

The RFM-220 Radio Modem is a high-speed packet modem and 220 MHz transceiver. When interfaced to the external modem connector on most standard TNCs, the RFM-220 can be used to send and receive data at 19,200 baud. The RFM-220 also can be used as a channelized 220 MHz FM voice radio. The RFM-220 lists for $995.95.

Fig. 9-4. The AEA HF Modem, PM-1.

PKT-1

The PKT-1 was the first TAPR TNC-1 clone. However, it differs in many respects from the original TAPR design. These differences include no parallel port (one was available as an option), no wire wrap area, 12 Vdc operation, and a 5-pin radio connector with redundant audio and AFSK outputs. The PKT-1 uses the full TAPR TNC-1 command set and is operationally compatible with the TAPR TNC-1. List price was $499.00 (Fig. 9-5).

The PKT-1 is virtually identical to the TNC-1. There are plated holes on the printed circuit board for the mounting of the parallel port components. The user interface is almost identical to the TAPR TNC-1's; however, all references to TAPR have been replaced with AEA. The owner's manual is not nearly as extensive as the one included with the TAPR TNC-1, and a second technical manual is available as an option from AEA. The PKT-1 is no longer manufactured.

Fig. 9-5. The AEA PKT-1.

Pakratt 64

The PK-64 is an excellent example of a machine-specific data communications device. It connects to the cartridge port of a Commodore 64 or 128. This unit not only operates packet but also CW, RTTY, and AMTOR. For HF work, the optional HFM-64 (high frequency modem) is recommended. The HFM-64 installs inside the PK-64 and replaces the internal PLL modem for HF operation. The HFM-64 adds a tuning indicator and threshold control to the front panel of the PK-64 (Fig. 9-6).

Fig. 9-6. The AEA PK-64.

There is no software necessary in the Commodore; all software is included in the PK-64. The user interface of the PK-64 uses function keys and parameter screens. It also includes a download buffer and tuning indicator and uses the TAPR command set. Like the PKT-1, the PK-64 includes a 5-pin radio connector and redundant audio plugs. The list price was $219.95 for the basic PK-64. The PK-64 is no longer manufactured.

Bill Ashby and Son
PAC/NET board

The PAC/NET is a TNC board similar in design to the VADCG TNC. It does not include a modem and utilizes its own user interface. Prices range from $80 to $240, depending on configuration. These boards are not in widespread use anymore.

DRSI
PC*Packet Adapter

The DRSI PC*Packet Adapter is a dual-port packet radio TNC that plugs into an IBM PC or compatible computer (Fig. 9-7). The PC*Packet Adapter has an on-board 1,200-baud modem for VHF operation. A second output, which can be configured for either RS-232 or TTL signals, can be interfaced to an external modem, such as the HF*Modem. The PC*Packet Adapter lists for $139.95.

*Fig. 9-7. The DRSI PC*Packet card.*

DRSI

HF*Modem

The DRSI HF*Modem is a 300-baud modem and tuning indicator that can be inter-faced to DRSI's PC*Packet Adapter for HF operation (Fig. 9-8). The HF*Modem also can be used with any standard TNC-2 via a modem disconnect adapter available from DRSI. The HF*Modem lists for $79.95.

*Fig. 9-8. The DRSI HF*Modem.*

GLB

PK-1

The GLB PK-1 was the first commercially produced TNC, introduced in August 1983. The PK-1 does not include any status indicator other than a power-on indicator. The PK-1 implements HDLC in software, so when a frame is being disassembled the pro-cessor is running at close to full capacity. Therefore, when the unit is accepting input from the user via the RS-232 port, it cannot disassemble incoming frames. The PK-1 came in a variety of configurations. List prices ranged from $109.95 to $169.95.

PK-1L

The PK-1L is a portable, low-power version of the PK-1. It draws about 25 mA @ 12 Vdc, making it ideal for portable operation. As in the case of the PK-1, the PK-1L does not have any status indicators (not even a power-on indicator). The unit can be powered for several hours from an ordinary 9 Vdc battery (Figs. 9-9 and 9-10). List price is $209.95.

Netlink 220

The GLB Netlink 220 is a high-speed modem operating on the 220 MHz band (Fig. 9-11). The Netlink 220 can be interfaced to any TNC-2 via the external modem con-

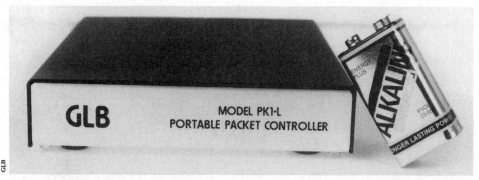

Fig. 9-9. The GLB PK-1L.

Fig. 9-10. A portable packet station incorporating the PK-1L. The perfboard to the right of the Model 100 is a PTT controller for the IC-02AT.

nector. Transmission speed is 19,200 baud, and turnaround time (from transmit to receive and back) is about 1 ms. The Netlink 220 lists for $699.95.

TNC-2A

The TNC-2A is another TAPR TNC-2 clone. The only differences between the TAPR TNC-2 and the GLB TNC-2A is that GLB has replaced the cylindrical RAM backup battery with a flat button cell and the unit has a slightly different cabinet. The TNC-2A came only in kit form, and the list price was $169.95.

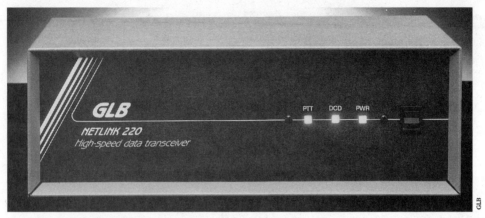

Fig. 9-11. The GLB Netlink 220.

HAL
PCI-3000

The PCI-3000 is a full-length card for IBM PCs that incorporates AMTOR, Baudot RTTY, ASCII RTTY, and CW. The card comes with the necessary software for operating all the supported modes. The PCI-3000 lists for $395.00.

RPC-2000

The HAL RPC-2000 is a dual-port packet radio TNC contained on a full-length IBM PC card. A VHF modem is included on board, and an external modem, such as the ST-7000, can be interfaced to the second port.

SPT-1

The SPT-1 Spectra-Tune is a multimode tuning indicator for use with RTTY, AMTOR, fax, SSTV, and CW. It interfaces simply via an audio cable and lists for $169.00.

ST-7000

The HAL ST-7000 HF Packet Modem is designed specifically for 300-baud HF packet operation. The ST-7000 contains a built-in tuning indicator and is fully compatible with all existing TNCs. It lists for $299.00.

Hamilton Area Packet Network
HAPN Packet Adapter

The HAPN packet adapter is a plug-in TNC for IBM PC and compatible microcomputers. The HAPN packet adapter plugs directly into one of the slots in the PC and contains a built-in modem, which interfaces to a radio via a DB-9 connector. The

HAPN packet adapter is capable of running AX.25, V-1, and V-2. List cost is $199 for an assembled and tested board with AX.25 software.

Heathkit
HK-232

The Heathkit HK-232 PackKit is Heathkit's licensed kit version of AEA's PK-232. The HK-232 is electrically identical to the PK-232, but its case, although following the same layout, is cosmetically different from the PK-232 (Fig. 9-12). The HK-232 in kit form lists for $279.95, a 12 Vdc power supply is $19.95, and an optional technical manual is $24.95.

Fig. 9-12.   The Heathkit HK-232.

HK-21

The Heathkit HK-21 is an interesting device—a pocket-sized TNC (Fig. 9-13). It is ideal for all VHF packet portable situations, including the Space Shuttle Sarex operation. The HK-21 is TNC-2 software compatible and also includes a built-in mailbox system. It is smaller than a pack of cigarettes, and optional battery pack can be installed inside the unit, eliminating the need for an external power supply. A regular RS-232 port is provided for interfacing to almost any terminal, such as a portable computer. Two radio interface methods are provided: direct mic and speaker cables for most HTs with full PTT control and a conventional port for interfacing with other transceivers. The HK-21 lists for $219.95, and the optional battery pack is $17.95.

Fig. 9-13. The Heathkit HK-21.

HD-4040

The HD-4040 was another TAPR TNC-1 clone and came in kit form (Fig. 9-14). It was identical to the TAPR TNC-1 in all respects. The list price was approximately $250.

Fig. 9-14. The Heathkit HD-4040.

Kantronics

Data Engine

The Kantronics Data Engine is a versatile platform for advanced packet radio systems. The basic Data Engine comes equipped for 1,200 baud AX.25 operation. However, a second modem can be added for dual-port operation. A variety of modems are available with data rates up to 19,200 baud. The Data Engine is based on an Intel-compatible V40 microprocessor running at 10 MHz and comes with 64 K of RAM, expandable to 512 K. The EPROM socket is capable of supporting up to an additional 512 K of firmware.

KAM

The Kantronics All Mode (KAM) is Kantronics' answer to AEA's PK-232 (Fig. 9-15). The KAM operates on the following modes: facsimile, CW, RTTY (both ASCII and Baudot), VHF and HF packet, and AMTOR. A built-in tuning indicator and dual-ports for the simultaneous connection of a VHF and HF radio are provided.

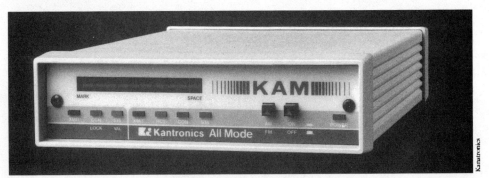

Fig. 9-15. The Kantronics KAM (Kantronics All Mode).

Kantronics also markets proprietary terminal software for use with the KAM (as with most of its other TNCs). The 64-Combo, which includes both terminal and facsimile programs, is available for the Commodore 64 and 128 computers. HostMaster II, a terminal program designed for multimode operation, and Superfax II, for facsimile reception and storage, are available for the IBM PC and compatibles. The KAM lists for $319.

KPC-2

The Kantronics Packet Communicator-2 (KPC-2) is a revised model of the company's original KPC (Fig. 9-16). It is somewhat similar to the TAPR TNC-2 and uses an almost identical user interface. List price is $219.95.

Fig. 9-16. The Kantronics KPC-2.

The KPC-2 modem section is easily switched between VHF and HF tones; however, no tuning indicator is provided. The KPC-2 runs on 12 Vdc. The RS-232 connector does have two nonstandard pins, which can interfere with your terminal if they are connected.

KPC-4

The Kantronics Packet Communicator-4 (KPC-4) is a true dual-port TNC with two simultaneously operable radio ports. Automatic gateway operation between ports is provided. Crossband and in-band split gateway operation are possible, or two independent packet connections can be made, one on each port. The KPC-4 lists for $329.

KPC-2400

The Kantronics Packet Communicator-2400 (KPC-2400) includes the 300-baud and 1,200-baud KPC-2 modem, in addition to a 2,400-bps PSK modem. The PSK modem operates at 1,200 baud with a signaling rate of 2,400-bps (Fig. 9-17). The list price is $329.

Fig. 9-17. The Kantronics KPC-2400.

2400 TNC Modem

The Kantronics 2400 TNC Modem is an external 2,400-bps modem card for the TAPR TNC-1 and TNC-2 and their clones. These modem cards attach to the external modem connector on the TNCs and allow them to communicate with the KPC-2400, as well as other similarly equipped TNCs at 2,400 bps. The list price is $149.

L.L. Grace
DSP-12

The L.L. Grace DSP-12 uses a Motorola DSP56001 DSP processor and a V40 PC-compatible processor. The DSP-12 presently supports over 40 modem standards for HF and VHF packet, RTTY, ASCII, and satellite. New standards can be added by a firmware update or downloaded into RAM. The DSP-12 sells for $595, and a one-megabyte memory expansion is $149.

MFJ
1214

The MFJ 1214 is a multimode interface that incorporates fax, Baudot RTTY, ASCII RTTY, and CW. The included software (for either IBM, Amiga, or Atari ST computers) is menu driven and includes many fax features, including color fax reception. The MFJ-1214 lists for $149.95.

1270B

The MFJ 1270B is MFJ's latest version of its 1270 TNC-2 clone (Fig. 9-18). The 1270B features TNC-2-compatible firmware, and lists for $139.95.

Fig. 9-18. The MFJ 1274 (upper) and MFJ 1270B (bottom).

1274

The MFJ 1274 is a VHF/HF TNC (Fig. 9-18). The 1274 is basically a 1270B with a built-in HF modem and tuning indicator. It lists for $169.95.

1278

The MFJ 1278 is MFJ's multimode data controller (Fig. 9-19). Similar to the AEA PK-232 and Kantronics KAM, the 1278 features operation on HF and VHF packet, Baudot and ASCII RTTY, CW, facsimile, and SSTV. The 1278 also has a built-in contest memory keyer. The SSTV and fax modes allow for both the transmission and reception of images. The 1278 lists for $249.95.

1273

The MFJ-1273 is a TAPR-compatible tuning indicator, which plugs into the TAPR tuning indicator connector on most TNC-1s, TNC-2s, and clones. The 1273 lists for $49.95.

Fig. 9-19. The MFJ 1278.

Microlog
ART-1

The Microlog ART-1 is an all-mode digital interface for the Commodore 64 and 128 microcomputers. It comes equipped for CW, RTTY, and AMTOR operation; packet capability is available as an option. The ART-1 packet option uses either TAPR-compatible commands or unique Microlog commands. The list price is $199.

Pac-Comm
HandiPacket

The HandiPacket is a small, self-contained packet TNC ideal for use in portable applications. The HandiPacket comes with internal battery pack and charger, belt clip, and all cables. In fact, the HandiPacket has been used aboard the Soviet MIR space station. The HandiPacket lists for $229.95.

TNC-220

The Pac-Comm TNC-220 was designed to be a successor to the TNC-200 and other TAPR TNC-2 clones. It features a single-chip modem section that is software configurable between two radio ports. The standard configuration supports one HF and one VHF radio port, each with its own radio cable connector. Switching between ports is done entirely in software, so no cable switching or retuning is required. The modem includes a bypass header for addition of an external modem. The TNC-220 uses the TAPR command set and supports AX.25.

TNC-320

The TNC-320 is the successor to the TNC-220. The TNC-320 is designed for both HF and VHF/UHF use. It uses a Z-80 microprocessor, 32 K EPROM, 32 K nonvolatile RAM, and a duplex HDLC. The TNC-320 lists for $209.95.

TINY-2

Pac-Comm's TINY-2 is an improved version of the TAPR TNC-2 (Fig. 9-20). The TINY-2 comes with TAPR firmware and is NET/ROM compatible. It lists for $119.95.

Fig. 9-20. The Pac-Comm TINY-2.

MICROPOWER-2

The Pac-Comm MICROPOWER-2 is a low-power version of the TINY-2, consuming about 40 mA at 9 to 12 Vdc (Fig. 9-21). The MICROPOWER-2 lists for $159.95.

Fig. 9-21. *The Pac-Comm MICROPOWER-2.*

TNC-200

The Pac-Comm TNC-200 is another TAPR TNC-2 clone (Fig. 9-22). The link and terminal baud rates are set via DIP switches on the back panel. The modem configuration can be changed by altering components mounted on a *DIP header* (a device that allows for the mounting of discrete components and plugs into an IC socket). List prices range from $39.95 for a bare board and manual to $219.95 for an assembled and tested CMOS version with power supply.

The TNC-200 comes in a variety of configurations, both kit and assembled. It runs on 12 Vdc. The radio port is a 5-pin DIN socket. The TNC-200 is a good, reliable TNC-2 clone.

Fig. 9-22. *The Pac-Comm TNC-200.*

PC-120

The PC-120 is a TNC on a half-size IBM PC card. It includes TNC software and built-in modems, along with RS-232 interfaces for external modems (Fig. 9-23).

Fig. 9-23. The Pac-Comm PC-120 card.

PC-320

The PC-320 is an intelligent TNC on a full-size IBM PC card. Unlike the PC-120, the PC-320 includes an on-board microprocessor and can even be operated with the computer powered down. The PC-320 operates on both VHF and HF and includes the necessary software programs for the IBM PC. The PC-320 lists for $209.95.

Surface-Mount TNC

Pac-Comm has been working on an ultraminiature surface-mount TNC (Fig. 9-24). This TNC is small enough to be installed inside the case of some HTs. Pac-Comm also markets miniature internal data modems. The Pac-Comm HT-1200 is a 1,200-baud modem with a TTL digital interface. The Pac-Comm HT-232 is an RS-232-level converter for the HT-1200.

DR-100/DR-200

The Pac-Comm DR-100 and DR-200 are packet radio switch/repeater modules that have been designed for dedicated network support service. The DR-100 is a single-port device that functions as a low-cost single-frequency digital repeater. The DR-200

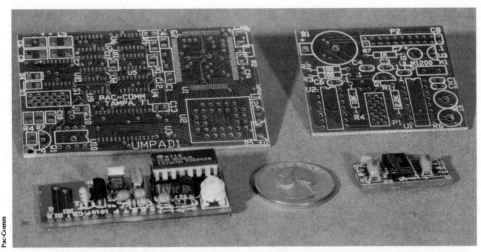

Fig. 9-24. The Pac-Comm ultraminiature TNC circuit board (upper left); the TNC's 1,200 baud modem circuit board (upper right); the HT-1200 (lower left); a quarter (lower middle); the HT-232 (lower right).

is a dual-port design. The DR-100 may be upgraded to dual-port capability. Both units are based on the Z-80 microprocessor with a capacity of 32 K each of ROM and battery-backed RAM. Provisions are included for the addition of an RS-232-compatible terminal. The DR-100 and DR-200 are provided with user-selected software.

MacPacket

MacPacket is a packet terminal program for the Apple Macintosh computer. It features a split screen, receive buffer, menus, and digipeater routing tables. List price is $49.95.

Richcraft Engineering

Robert Richardson W4UCH developed a packet radio software program for TRS-80 models I, III, and IV microcomputers. The only necessary hardware is a modem and radio. The software turns the computer into a functional TNC. Two systems are available: VADCG and AX.25. Although the Richcraft system enjoyed some popularity during the early period of packet radio development, it is not in widespread use anymore.

Software 2000

Software 2000's NET/ROM is a very popular level 3 networking system developed by Mike Busch W6IXU and Ron Raikes WA8DED. NET/ROM comes on an EPROM chip that simply replaces the ROM chip in TNC-2-compatible TNCs. Contact Software 2000 for pricing and licensing information.

S. Fine Software
Macket

Macket is a powerful packet telecommunications program for the Apple Macintosh and runs on the 512 K, 512e, MacPlus, Mac SE, and Mac II computers. Extensive windowing, special host mode support for many TNCs, and uploading and downloading are some of its many features. Macket will work with any data communications interface with an RS-232 port. It lists for $39.95.

TAPR
TNC-1

The TAPR TNC-1 is the de facto standard for all present hardware TNCs. The TAPR TNC-1 bridged the gap between the earlier hardcore packet radio experimenters and today's more user-oriented operators. The TAPR TNC-1 was the TNC that opened the world of packet radio to thousands of amateurs.

The TNC-1 uses a 6809 microprocessor and features LED status indicators, a parallel status port, and an RS-232 serial I/O port. The TNC-1 uses nonvolatile RAM (NOVRAM) for the storage of permanent parameters such as callsign, transmitter delay, and retries. A wire-wrap area is provided for modifications. The modem was designed with certain components mounted on DIP headers so that modem configuration could be changed by simply changing headers.

The software implements both AX.25 Version 1 and VADCG V-1. Up to 8 digipeaters are allowed. The user interface was designed to be as user friendly as possible.

The manual is written with the first-time packet operator in mind, including a tutorial that introduces new users to packet radio. Several technical sections allow the manual to serve as a technical reference for advanced operators. The assembly section is detailed and sufficient graphics that are included to guide the user painlessly through the assembly process.

Although the TNC-1 is no longer produced by TAPR, its expansive user base and the proliferation of clones guarantee its continuing place in amateur packet radio.

TNC-2

The TNC-2 was developed by TAPR to overcome some of the inherent disadvantages of the TNC-1. Although the TNC-1 was (and is) an excellent unit, it was rather expensive, large, and required 110 V. TAPR sought a new TNC with a lower cost, 12 Vdc operation, smaller size, and lower weight. The result of their efforts was the TNC-2.

The TNC-2 had a host of new features not available previously. The TNC-2 was the first TNC to fully implement AX.25 Version 2. The monitor command and capabilities were increased. A real-time clock allowed time stamping of incoming packets, and all parameters were saved with battery-backed RAM.

The hardware of the TNC-2 also differed from that used in the TNC-1. A Z-80 microprocessor was chosen for the TNC-2, partially because of the large amount of software development systems available for it. The modem section remained virtually identical to the TNC-1's. The TNC-2 required only a single 12 Vdc supply, rather than access to 110 V.

Like the TNC-1, the TNC-2 has been licensed and widely copied. The TNC-2 set a new standard for amateur packet radio TNCs.

VADCG
TNC+

The VADCG TNC+ is a revised version of the original VADCG TNC (Fig. 9-25). The TNC+ comes in kit form with parts for $168.

WA8DED

Ronald Raikes WA8DED developed an alternative software with a different command set and user interface for the TAPR TNC-1 and compatibles. His program fits on two EPROMs and plugs into the ROM sockets on the TNC-1 in place of the TAPR ROMs.

The WA8DED firmware allows multiple connections and monitoring of all frame types. All commands are 1 or 2 letters, and whenever possible, they are modeled after the TAPE command abbreviations. The WA8DED software is in the public domain for noncommercial use and is available from a variety of sources.

Fig. 9-25. The VADCG TNC+.

Conclusion

There are bound to be many products that I have not covered in this chapter. That does not mean that I have purposely excluded them for any particular reason; rather, because of space and time considerations, I am limited in the number of products I can include.

10

The future of digital communications

DIGITAL COMMUNICATIONS MODES ARE A RAPIDLY EVOLVING PART OF AMATEUR RADIO. Although many advancements have been made in digital communications technology over the years, especially since the introduction of packet radio, many more improvements are still in the works. These changes will provide additional capabilities and expand the usefulness of digital modes. This chapter introduces areas of current development and areas that might see development in the future.

Most of the current development work is being directed at packet radio. Many new areas of packet radio are being explored and developed, including packet hardware, software, and protocols. In the area of hardware, work is underway on developing high-speed modems, digital transceivers, integrated TNCs, and higher-level protocols. Changes such as diminished VHF DX operation, growth of local networks, UHF and VHF gateways, and level-3 networks have reduced packet congestion. Improved operating practices on packet also can be expected.

High-speed modems

Work on high-speed modems has been going on for many years, spurred on by packet radio enthusiasts. The Bell 202 standard was chosen for amateur packet operation on the VHF and UHF bands because of the readily available components, the ease of interfacing with most radios, and the availability of components on the surplus market. The 1,200-baud transmission speed is a big improvement over the 300-baud and lower speeds usually used in amateur digital communications. However, as packet radio grew, and continues to grow, even 1,200 baud is not fast enough.

With many users sharing the same channel, it is beneficial to minimize transmission time. Also, higher transmission speeds reduce the time required for long file and message transfers. There are alternatives to 1,200-baud Bell 202 modems being proposed and introduced, but developing and selecting one optimum for packet operation has not been easy.

Because VHF and UHF links are usually reliable and interference-free, better modulation techniques and much higher speeds are possible. Limitations are imposed by FCC regulations, as well as the TNCs and transceivers being used. By using a modulation technique such as PSK, in which more than one bit can be encoded per baud, high BPS rates can be obtained without a significant increase in bandwidth. Many transceivers may require modifications to enable them to be used with high-speed modems. These modifications might include the removal or bypass of filters and other components designed to support voice transmission and reception. Since most amateurs will not want to modify their radios for packet use, modem systems that interface simply to the transceiver through the standard mic and audio connectors are most desirable.

Currently work is being done on 9,600-baud modems (direct FSK, 1 bit per baud) by several individuals and manufacturers. Initially, these modems will be used for backbone links between BBSs for networking purposes. Manufacturers, such as AEA and GLB have introduced commercial high-speed modems for packet use. At first these modems probably will be used for network linking only, but they may eventually filter down to individual users.

Digital radios

The problems associated with interfacing high-speed modems to regular-voice grade transceivers is being solved by the development of digital transceivers. Digital transceivers are being designed expressly for use with high-speed modems and, as such, their components are carefully chosen to meet this objective. These units have the modem and transceiver in a single case, ready to be connected to a TNC or other digital communications interface.

Taking the concept of digital radios one step further by also including the TNC in the unit is a distinct possibility. Interference problems might have to be resolved, but the advantages of reduced cables, a single power supply, and portability make the idea attractive.

Digital signal processing

Digital signal processing (DSP) has been around since the 1960s, but the recent development of specialized DSP integrated circuits has pushed the sophistication and practicality of DSP technology to new levels. The Motorola DSP56001 and the Texas Instruments TMS320C25 are two popular DSP chips.

For a variety of reasons, DSP technology has been popping up in electronics equipment over the past year. Some land-line modems now incorporate DSP, and Cincinnati Microwave's new Escort radar detector uses the Motorola DSP chip.

DSP has many specific applications, but most DSP systems follow some basic concepts. In this section, I'll discuss these basic concepts to develop a fundamental understanding of DSP technology. Keep in mind that some specific DSP systems may expand on or narrow their capabilities with respect to the following explanation.

DSP technology centers around the processing of discrete time signals. A *discrete time signal* is a quantifiable value at a given time. A discrete time data sequence is generated when the values of many discrete time signals are gathered at set time intervals. Many data sequences are intrinsically discrete in time, for example, the number of cars parked in a specific lot at noon.

However, we live in an analog world. Most events in nature do not take place in precise intervals. Rather, events take place continuously, over time. For example, the temperature does not change by 1-degree intervals. Rain does not fall in 1-inch increments. In the vast majority of cases, gathering a discrete time data sequence involves sampling.

Sampling is a very important concept in DSP. By sampling, we are able to convert analog, or continuous time, signals into discrete time signals. Sampling involves measuring an analog signal at a preset time interval. Through sampling, a discrete time data sequence can be obtained from a continuously varying analog signal. The sampling rate (how often the analog signal is measured), along with sampling resolution, determines how accurately the discrete time data sequence reflects the original analog signal.

When the analog signal is sampled, the value of the signal at that specific time is quantized. In essence, the value is recorded in digital form. For example, when a person says "On a scale of 1 to 10, I rate it a 6," he is quantizing. The resolution of the quantizing determines how accurately the digital sample reflects the original analog signal. The greater the resolution, the greater the accuracy of the sample.

In DSP systems, the sample is most often represented by a binary code. The greater the number of bits, the more exact the sample can be. A single bit gives a sampling resolution of 1 in 2, since one bit can either be 0 or 1. Five bits gives a sampling resolution of 1 in 32, and 8 bits yields 1 in 256. Just as a computer display with 256 colors looks better than one with 64 colors, which looks better than one with just 8 colors, a sample with 256 possible conditions is more accurate than one with just 64 or 2 possible conditions.

The ideal situation would be to sample as quickly as possible and with as much resolution as possible. This kind of sampling would yield the most accurate reflection of the original analog signal. Unfortunately, we are limited by processing power to how fast and how exact sampling can be done. Additionally, if it was necessary to retain this quantized data sequence, copious amounts of data would have to be stored. Thus, there are limits to the sampling and quantizing processes.

What we've covered so far is only the beginning of digital signal processing. Once the desired analog signal has been converted to a discrete time data sequence, it is processed. How it is processed depends entirely on what the DSP system is designed to do. Some simple applications include filtering out "abnormal" variations in the analog signal, such as noise or interference. Filtering can be done by excluding or modifying samples that don't meet predetermined criteria. In fact, digital filters make up an important part of DSP technology.

Although all DSP involves filtering in one way or another, current amateur radio applications of DSP can be divided into 2 camps: filtering systems and modems. The filtering systems can be external additions to transceivers or built in. The DSP modems are the cornerstone of a new breed of multimode digital communication interfaces.

Kenwood currently has 2 DSP filtering systems available. The TS-950SD transceiver contains a built-in DSP filter system, and the company also makes the DSP-100, an add-on DSP filter system for the TS-850S transceiver. These DSP filters are capable of providing "unsurpassed receive and transmit performance that is not possible with analog processing," according to the company literature.

Although the DSP filter systems are wonderful technological advances, most of the interest of readers of this book is probably directed at the DSP multimode digital communication interfaces. These devices will prove a significant advance in amateur radio digital communications. Their primary advantage is their ability to emulate almost any modem standard.

Imagine being able to use one interface to communicate with a variety of modulation systems. Current multimode interfaces such as the PK-232 and KAM contain 2 separate modem systems: one for HF and one for VHF. These systems allow them to operate the standard digital modes, but they are not capable of communicating with newly developed modulation standards without the use of an external modem. By having a DSP multimode interface, the single DSP modem could be programmed to emulate almost any modulation standard.

In fact, with DSP, it is very easy to play around with the modulation characteristics. You could develop your own standard or simply optimize the modem for a specific use. DSP allows a great deal of flexibility. It no longer would be necessary to change modem headers or add a new external modem to alter an interface's modem characteristics. Using DSP technology, you could write your own modem in software; simply tell the DSP section what you want it to do.

The advantages of DSP multimode interfaces should be fairly clear by now. With a one-time investment, you would be able to operate all current modem standards. Currently, if you want to operate the Microsats, you have to purchase an external modem designed to work with their standards. To operate a high-speed packet link, you have to add another external modem or two. And if there are any new standards, you'd have to buy another modem or modify the one you already have. Additionally, the DSP modems would, in all probability, prove superior in performance to the standard modems we're presently using in our interfaces.

Amateur radio digital satellites

A recent flurry of satellite launches promises many additional capabilities to amateur digital communications operators. Worldwide networking is feasible via satellite. Individual users can access the satellites directly or through shared ground-based gateway stations equipped to automatically track the satellites and relay all traffic sent to the gateway through the satellite selected. For more information on amateur satellites and operating conditions, consult *The Satellite Experimenter's Handbook* by Martin Davidoff listed in the bibliography or contact AMSAT.

One of the packet satellites is the Phase III-C, now known as OSCAR 13, which was launched into a highly elliptical orbit on June 15, 1988, from French Guiana. OSCAR 13 contains a device known as RUDAK, which serves as a space-borne digipeater. RUDAK, which was designed by the West German affiliate of AMSAT, contains memory for use as buffers and for future uploading of programs from the ground. The program space gives RUDAK the ability to adjust to new protocols or operating conditions. The uplink to RUDAK is 2,400-baud PSK and the downlink is 400-baud PSK. Because of the modulation characteristics chosen, special modems will be needed for use by ground stations that want to communicate with RUDAK.

Another packet satellite is known as Fuji OSCAR 12 (FO-12). Originally called JAS-1, Fuji was launched in early August 1986. Fuji was developed by JAMSAT, the Japanese affiliate of AMSAT, and features an on-board flying mailbox similar to terrestrial packet BBSs.

Fuji carries two separate Mode-J transponders: 2-meter uplink and 70-cm downlink. The JA transponder is a standard linear transponder similar to those on current amateur satellites. It is a digital transponder featuring 4 input channels using Manchester-coded FM. There is one downlink channel using PSK. The AX.25 Version 2 protocol is used and the bps rate is 1,200.

Other satellites of interest to digital communications enthusiasts are the recent UoSATs and Microsats. These satellites were all launched together as secondary payload on an Ariane launch vehicle in January 1990. The satellites are UO-14, UO-15, AO-16, DO-17, WO-18, and LO-19. The two UoSATs—UoSAT OSCAR 14 and UoSAT OSCAR 15—were developed by the University of Surrey in England and AMSAT-UK. AO-16, or AMSAT OSCAR 16, is also known as PACSAT, for Packet Satellite. AO-16 is a digital store-and-forward packet radio BBS and features 4 uplink channels on 2 meters and two downlink channels on 70 cm. The data format is AX.25 at 1,200 or 4,800 bps PSK. LO-19, for LUSAT OSCAR 19, is virtually identical to AO-16, with the exception of a CW beacon. Information on operating frequencies for these satellites is included in appendix E.

DO-17, or DOVE OSCAR 17, does not have a transponder. It was designed to transmit a beacon in both digitized voice and regular AFSK AX.25 at 1,200 bps in the 2-m band. Figure 10-1 shows some DO-17 telemetry that I monitored. DO-17 provides an easy way to experiment with most phases of satellite operation. By the way, DOVE stands for Digital Orbiting Voice Encoder.

WEBBERSAT OSCAR 18, or WO-18, also does not have a transponder. The unique feature of WO-18 is its video camera. Using the appropriate software, it is possible to display pictures taken from space on a personal computer with data from WO-18. WO-18 has two downlink channels for the picture data and telemetry. WO-18's data format is AX.25 transmitted at 1,200 bps PSK.

Yet another satellite of interest is Fuji-2, a second Japanese satellite that is virtually identical to the first Fuji mentioned earlier. Fuji-2 is known as FO-20, for Fuji OSCAR 20, and was launched about two weeks after the Microsats, in February 1990.

We are extremely fortunate to have so many satellites available for our use. However, one area of concern from an operating standpoint is compatibility. Many different modulation characteristics are in use, requiring ground stations to have dif-

```
DOVE-1>LSTAT:I P:0x3000 o:0 1:13081 f:13081, d:0

DOVE-1>WASH:wash addr:3680:0000, edac=0x88

DOVE-1>TIME-1:PHT: uptime is 158/00:55:11.  Time is Tue Jan
08 03:06:15 1991

DOVE-1>TLM:00:5A 01:5A 02:86 03:31 04:58 05:58 06:6E 07:53
08:6C 09:74 0A:A30B:DA 0C:E8 0D:D8 0E:02 0F:24 10:D4 11:A9
12:02 13:02 14:A4 15:8E16:8A 17:85 18:88 19:89 1A:88 1B:6F
1C:8B 1D:89 1E:2A 1F:5F 20:BD

DOVE-1>WASH:wash addr:3880:0000, edac=0x88

DOVE-1>TLM:21:AE 22:88 23:24 24:1F 25:29 26:00 27:01 28:01
29:01 2A:01 2B:002C:01 2D:27 2E:01 2F:9B 30:CA 31:9E 32:12
33:D6 34:BD 35:97 36:A437:A4 38:AE

DOVE-1>STATUS: 80 00 00 97 00 18 CC 02 00 B0 00 00 0B 0D 3C
05 0B 00 04 04
```

Fig. 10-1. DO-17 (Dove) telemetry.

ferent modems for different satellites. Fortunately, manufacturers are starting to come to our aid. Pac-Comm has introduced a Microsat PSK modem that will also receive 400-baud telemetry. Within a short time, we should see more commercial alternatives to homebrewing a modem for each satellite. The emerging field of digital signal processing is already providing devices that are capable of emulating the multitude of modem standards.

SAREX 2

Another area of digital space communications is the SAREX 2, Shuttle Amateur Radio Experiment, packet radio experiment. SAREX 1 was the SSTV experiment flown on Spacelab 1. Following the successful operation of FM and SSTV from the space shuttle, several packet operators began to formulate a plan to place an amateur packet station aboard the space shuttle. NASA was cooperative and, based on the success of the earlier amateur radio operations from the space shuttle, approved the packet experiment concept.

The current SAREX 2 hardware is a Motorola 2-m HT, a Heathkit HK-21 "pocket packet" TNC, and a Grid laptop computer. The result is an automated packet station for use on the shuttle, which will allow stations to connect to it, receive their contact number, and automatically disconnect. A terminal mode is also included so that the astronaut can conduct live QSOs.

Software and protocols

Although the future for digital communications hardware looks bright, let's not overlook the software, protocols, and networks necessary to make the hardware function. These nonhardware developments can take many forms.

User interfaces

User interfacing is an area of programming that has seen a great deal of effort. As more features are included in digital communications interface units, the need for increasingly user-friendly interfaces has developed. Today's multimode units, such as the PK-232 and the KAM, have many different operating modes that all must be controlled via the user interface and its command set.

Although long lists of sometimes cryptic commands are now necessary to allow complete control of digital communications interfaces, many users want more informative commands within the user interface than, for example, a CMD: prompt. Menus, help screens, and tutorials would be a great help to many users attempting to learn the system.

A new generation of user interfaces should be developed that will meet the needs of the casual operator. In the case of machine-specific interfaces, advanced user interfaces could be programmed in with the rest of the command set. However, in universal hardware interfaces, where the primary objective is compatibility with different terminal systems, a higher-level user interface will have to be developed for specific terminal systems. This high-level user interface, actually a specialized terminal program written for a specific personal computer and digital communications unit (such as an IBM-PC and an AEA PK-232), will handle all communications with the digital communications unit. The user will not see the individual commands or the CMD: prompt. Rather, the user will be presented with a series of windows, menus, or whatever fits best with the specific computer system being used as a terminal.

For example, to initiate a connect, the user would simply position the cursor over CONNECT on the menu and press RETURN. The user could then be prompted to enter the appropriate calls and relay stations if necessary. To change a parameter, the user could select another menu and then select the appropriate parameter. Since the parameters will probably vary for VHF, HF, and satellite work, entire stations setups could be saved on disk and then recalled when needed, rather than having to change the parameters each time.

By having an option in the software to select different digital communication units, the same program could be used with TNCs with different command sets, in much the same way as a word processor can be configured to print with different printers. Thus, a user would not have to learn a different command set for every TNC used.

I'm happy to say that many of these ideas and concepts are being incorporated into specialized amateur radio digital communications software today. Programs such as Steve Fine's Macket, a high-level user interface written for the Macintosh, incorporate many of these concepts. Not only will these programs make operating easier for users now, but they will go a long way toward attracting new users, who have been put off by the complexity of operating.

Protocols

Protocols have been an area of concern and development since the beginning of packet radio. Today, the physical and data link layers are well defined and established as a result of many years of work. Now it's time for the next step up the ladder with the network, transport, session, and possibly the presentation and application layers in the years ahead.

Many protocols in existence might be acceptable to the amateur packet radio environment. The problem is knowing what features we need, what features we do not, and the best way to implement those we do. The OSI/RM provides an excellent frame of reference for designing a network, but it is not cast in stone. It is possible that in the future, amateur packet radio might handle the high-level protocols in a different manner. For now, however, we appear to be proceeding according to the OSI/RM.

Currently, most of the developmental work is being directed toward a network layer protocol. Developments such as NET/ROM demonstrate the progress that is being made. Level-4 and -5 protocols are also under study, and there are several proposals, but no firm commitment at this time.

Networking

The future of packet radio will see many changes in the way we can use the amateur packet radio network. Packet operating practices have been evolving to reflect the many new capabilities the amateur packet radio system has been gaining. Currently, our operating practices for the existing packet network have been causing severe congestion in heavily populated areas, due, in most part, to our current practice of overusing 1 or 2 channels.

Because most BBSs are on the same channel (for mail forwarding), most users tend to congregate on the same channel out of habit or to monitor BBS activity. Digipeaters are also on the frequency to allow for expanded mail forwarding and increased communications range. The current tendency is to have much of the activity taking place on the BBS channel. When new users arrive, there is no other active channel, so they join in. As a result, the congestion is unbearable and, at times, no traffic can get through.

Fortunately, this situation is changing in many areas of the country as solutions are implemented. By spreading out the activity over a number of channels, the congestion on each channel is much lower. In one approach, 2-m FM channels are left to individual users for keyboard-to-keyboard communications, file transfers, and experimentation. Another channel is kept for BBS use only.

With this system, using current technology, congestion problems can be reduced by expanding the number of channels proportional to the number of users. One disadvantage is that a single station cannot monitor activity on all the channels at once, as was done when all activity occurred on a single channel. But that is a small price to pay for the reduced congestion.

The network will need to adapt as new hardware, such as high-speed modems, is implemented. High-speed modems could be used first for BBS forwarding and long-haul linking. In the transition period, these foreign modems would thus be hidden from the individual users.

One potential problem with a network based on many users on different channels in the same area is linking with other stations using current digipeater technology. Each user will have to keep a list of what digipeaters on what channels will take him to the desired destination. If there is a choice of two or more paths, how do you know which is the best to choose? How do you know which channel your friends are on at any given time?

These problems are being solved by the addition of level-3 packet switches (network nodes). We are seeing the evolution of this concept with the proliferation of pseudo-level-3 node systems such as NET/ROM. The use of network nodes is giving rise to the local area packet network.

Users in a certain area will operate on the same frequency. Other users in a separate area will operate on a different frequency so they won't interfere. Users in one area will communicate with users in another area through the network nodes. It does not matter if the area is a few miles away, a few hundred miles away, or a few thousand miles away; the network node will choose the optimum route to get the data to the proper destination. The route could include VHF, UHF, satellite, HF, or a combination thereof.

All the individual user will need to know is the location of the station he wishes to communicate with; the network node will determine how to reach it. VHF DX operation will no longer be necessary, nor will connecting to a station through an inordinate number of digipeaters. However, digipeaters might still be necessary for users who cannot reach their node directly.

The users in a given area will form a local area network (LAN) with their own BBS and possibly other facilities. Users will know where to reach their friends. With HF and satellites included in the network, worldwide networking will be possible.

The technology certainly exists to make this system a reality. All that is needed are funds, time, and volunteers. This network will make amateur packet radio a reliable and efficient means of worldwide communications. We have made considerable progress thus far, and there is no reason to believe we won't continue.

Digital imaging systems

Multimode digital communications interfaces brought about a new era in amateur digital communications. In addition to providing an easy way to work all the digital modes, they introduced the concept of digitized image transmission and reception to average users. Although fax and SSTV have been around for many years, most amateurs have never experimented with them. First with fax, and later SSTV, the multimode units provided an easy way to receive these images without the bother of thermal paper and video monitors.

Although not many amateurs bought their multimode units for their fax and SSTV capabilities, once set up and operating, many have been tempted to at least try these bonus features. The result is a surge of interest in fax and amateur television, both SSTV and fast scan TV. Manufacturers are now improving the digital imaging user interface on their units to make them easier to use, and at the same time, are adding increased capability and features. Although most agree that multimode digital units are not yet superior to independent fax and SSTV systems, the gap is narrowing. We can expect to see much more growth in this area in the years ahead.

Conclusion

Amateur radio digital communications is evolving rapidly. Packet radio is the primary motivating force, with the other modes benefiting from an overall increase of interest in digital communications in general. Each step that is made in developing packet radio helps to achieve the ultimate goal of a worldwide, error-free, efficient amateur radio data communications system. Each user adds to the whole and helps to shape its future. Most progress in amateur radio digital communications technology has been the result of dedicated work by individuals and groups, and will continue to be so in the future.

Appendix A

Morse code chart

MORSE CODE, NAMED AFTER ITS INVENTOR, SAMUEL MORSE, IS AN UNEVEN CODE made up of two elements: the dot (•), a short pulse, and the dash (—), a longer pulse. By combining dots (pronounced *dit*) and dashes (pronounced *dah*) in various orders, the alphabet, numerals, punctuation, and certain shorthand codes can be encoded. Listed here are all the characters in common use in the United States. For a complete list of all Morse code characters, including foreign-language and specialty codes, see the *ARRL Handbook*.

Character	Code	Character	Code
A	•—	P	•— —•
B	—•••	Q	— —•—
C	—•—•	R	•—•
D	—••	S	•••
E	•	T	—
F	••—•	U	••—
G	— —•	V	•••—
H	••••	W	•— —
I	••	X	—••—
J	•— — —	Y	—•— —
K	—•—	Z	— —••
L	•—••	1	•— — — —
M	— —	2	••— — —
N	—•	3	•••— —
O	— — —	4	••••—

Character	Code	Character	Code
5	••••—	.	•—•—•—
6	—••••	,	— —•• — —
7	— —•••	?	••— —••
8	— — —••	AR	•—•—• (End of message)
9	— — — —•	SK	•••—•— (End of communication)
0	— — — — —	BT	—•••— (Double dash)

Appendix B

Baudot code and AMTOR code charts

Baudot code

THE BAUDOT CODE IS A 5-LEVEL CODE WITH 32 POSSIBLE COMBINATIONS. BY shifting between 2 different character sets (called *letters* and *figures*), the number of possible combinations is doubled. As a result, the Baudot code can represent all 26 letters (no lowercase), 10 digits, some punctuation, and various control characters.

Combination number	Bit grouping	Letters case	Figures Case
01	00011	A	—
02	11001	B	?
03	01110	C	:
04	01001	D	$
05	00001	E	3
06	01101	F	!
07	11010	G	&
08	10100	H	#
09	00110	I	8
10	01011	J	' or bell
11	01111	K	(
12	10010	L	)
13	11100	M	.
14	01100	N	,
15	11000	O	9
16	10110	P	0
17	10111	Q	1

Combination number	Bit grouping	Letters case	Figures Case
18	01010	R	4
19	00101	S	bell or '
20	10000	T	5
21	00111	U	7
22	11110	V	; or =
23	10011	W	2
24	11101	X	/
25	10101	Y	6
26	10001	Z	+ or "
27	01000	Carriage return (CR)	
28	00010	Line feed (LF)	
29	11111	LTRS (letter shift)	
30	11011	FIGS (figure shift)	
31	00100	SP (space)	
32	00000	BLK (blank)	

AMTOR code

The AMTOR code is very similar to the Baudot code, as can be seen by comparing the Baudot code with the first 32 combinations of the AMTOR code. Also notice that there is a constant ratio of four 1's to three 0's in the AMTOR code. Since the AMTOR uses a 7-bit code, a total of 128 combinations are possible; however, limiting the code selections to those with four 1's and three 0's reduces the code choices to 35—which are all used in AMTOR. In addition, three of the codes serve double duty as control signals in ARQ operation (there is no confusion since they are only sent from the IRS to the ISS).

Combination number	Bit grouping	Letters case	Figures Case
01	1000111	A	—
02	1110010	B	?
03	0011101	C	:
04	1010011	D	
05	1010110	E	3
06	0011011	F	
07	0110101	G	
08	1101001	H	
09	1001101	I	8
10	0010111	J	bell
11	0011110	K	(
12	1100101	L	)
13	0111001	M	.

Combination number	Bit grouping	Letters case	Figures Case
14	1011001	N	,
15	1110001	O	9
16	0101101	P	0
17	0101110	Q	1
18	1010101	R	4
19	1001011	S	'
20	1110100	T	5
21	1001110	U	7
22	0111100	V	=
23	0100111	W	2
24	0111010	X	/
25	0101011	Y	6
26	1100011	Z	+
27	1111000	Carriage return (CR)	
28	1101100	Line feed (LF)	
29	1011010	LTRS (letters shift)	
30	0110110	FIGS (figures shift)	
31	1011100	SP (space)	
32	1101010	BLK (blank)	
33	0110011	Idle Beta	
34	0001111	Idle Alpha	
35	1100110	Signal reception	
12	1100101	CS1 (control signal 1)	
32	1101010	CS2 (control signal 2)	
09	1001101	CS3 (control signal 3)	

Appendix C

ASCII chart

THE FOLLOWING CHART PROVIDES THE DECIMAL AND HEXADECIMAL AMERICAN Standard Code for Information Interchange (ASCII) codes from 0 to 127. It may prove useful when setting the control characters on a terminal or TNC.

DEC	HEX	ASCII	DEC	HEX	ASCII
0	00	NUL	19	13	DC3(S)
1	01	SOH(A)	20	14	DC4(T)
2	02	STX(B)	21	15	NAK(U)
3	03	ETX(C)	22	16	SYN(V)
4	04	EOT(D)	23	17	ETB(W)
5	05	ENQ(E)	24	18	CAN(X)
6	06	ACK(F)	25	19	EM (Y)
7	07	BEL(G)	26	1A	SUB(Z)
8	08	BS (H)	27	1B	ESCAPE
9	09	HT (I)	28	1C	FS
10	0A	LF (J)	29	1D	GS
11	0B	VT (K)	30	1E	RS
12	0C	FF (L)	31	1F	US
13	0D	CR (M)	32	20	
14	0E	SO (N)	33	21	!
15	0F	SI (O)	34	22	"
16	10	DLE(P)	35	23	#
17	11	dc1(Q)	36	24	$
18	12	DC2(R)	37	25	%

DEC	HEX	ASCII	DEC	HEX	ASCII
38	26	&	83	53	S
39	27	'	84	54	T
40	28	(	85	55	U
41	29	)	86	56	V
42	2A	*	87	57	W
43	2B	+	88	58	X
44	2C	,	89	59	Y
45	2D	——	90	5A	Z
46	2E	.	91	5B	[
47	2F	/	92	5C	\
48	30	0	93	5D	]
49	31	1	94	5E	^
50	32	2	95	5F	–
51	33	3	96	60	
52	34	4	97	61	a
53	35	5	98	62	b
54	36	6	99	63	c
55	37	7	100	64	d
56	38	8	101	65	e
57	39	9	102	66	f
58	3A	:	103	67	g
59	3B	;	104	68	h
60	3C	<	105	69	i
61	3D	=	106	6A	j
62	3E	>	107	6B	k
63	3F	?	108	6C	l
64	40	@	109	6D	m
65	41	A	110	6E	n
66	42	B	111	6F	o
67	43	C	112	70	p
68	44	D	113	71	q
69	45	E	114	72	r
70	46	F	115	73	s
71	47	G	116	74	t
72	48	H	117	75	u
73	49	I	118	76	v
74	4A	J	119	77	w
75	4B	K	120	78	x
76	4C	L	121	79	y
77	4D	M	122	7A	z
78	4E	N	123	7B	{
79	4F	O	124	7C		
80	50	P	125	7D	}
81	51	Q	126	7E	~
82	52	R	127	7F	DELETE

Appendix D

The RS-232
C and D standards

ALTHOUGH THE RS-232 COMMUNICATIONS STANDARD WAS ORIGINALLY DEVELOPED in the late 1960s, it remains the standard interface specification for serial asynchronous communications equipment. Other standards have been developed that have advantages over RS-232, but the new standards have failed to supplant RS-232 because of its widespread use. The reason we, as amateur radio operators, are concerned with the RS-232 standard is because most microcomputers and terminals, as well as TNCs, multimode units, and other modem devices that are used in amateur digital communications, support RS-232 communications.

In serial asynchronous communications, digital signals are sent as groups of a specified length sequentially on a single channel, and uneven intervals between transmissions are allowed. The digital signals usually represent characters in text. Several standardized codes are in use today for the transmission of text data; ASCII (American Standard Code for Information Interchange) is the most common.

At first the RS-232 standard might seem a blessing because it seems to solve our serial communications needs very easily. After all, if two units each support RS-232, we can just wire them together and they will work; no problem. However, it is not that easy. Some so-called "RS-232 compatible" devices are not really very compatible. Compatibility is a matter of degrees; some devices are more compatible than others. This is definitely the case with most RS-232 implementations.

Some devices only support a subset of the RS-232 standard. Others vary pin assignments or voltage levels to meet their own requirements. Because of these potential problems, this appendix examines what the standards really standardize.

The RS-232 standard most probably will be encountered when connecting your hardware packet TNC or other digital modem device to your terminal or computer.

Should you run into problems with the interface, a thorough understanding of the RS-232 standard will help you in diagnosing the problem and coming up with a solution. A knowledge of the standard also can be very helpful when wiring RS-232 cables.

Introduction to the RS-232 Standard

The proper name for the RS-232 standard is "Interface Between Data Terminal Equipment and Data Communications Equipment Employing Serial Binary Data Interchange." The standard was developed by the Electronic Industries Association (EIA) and the latest version is D; thus the reference to RS-232D. However, because version D of the RS-232 standard is relatively new, you will continue to see references to version C for the foreseeable future. CCITT (*Comite Consultatif Internationale de Telegraphique et Telephonie*) Recommendation V.24 is almost identical to the RS-232C standard. This appendix will concentrate on the RS-232C standard because that version currently is being referenced by most microcomputer and peripheral manufacturers.

The RS-232C standard covers four main areas: the mechanical characteristics of the interface, the electrical signals across the interface, the function of each signal, and the subsets of signals used for certain applications.

Data terminal equipment (DTE) and *data communications equipment* (DCE), sometimes referred to as data circuit-terminating equipment, are the two device classifications in RS-232. A DTE is a terminal, a computer, or any device capable of transmitting and receiving data. A DCE is a device that establishes, maintains, and terminates a connection. A DCE also provides any necessary signal conversion between the data it receives from and sends to the terminal and the data it sends and receives over the communications channel. Telephone modems and packet radio TNCs are DCE devices. You will learn more about the physical differences between DTEs and DCEs later in this section.

There is no specific connector in the RS-232C standard. However, the DB-25 connector is most commonly used and is now included in the RS-232D standard. Virtually all hardware TNCs use the DB-25 connector as the port for terminal communications. The DCE usually has the female connector, DB-25S (socket). The maximum recommended cable length is 50 ft and the maximum cable capacitance is 2,500 pF. Cable runs of greater than 50 ft are appropriate provided the load capacitance measured at the interface point and including the signal terminator does not exceed 2,500 pF.

Signals

RS-232 electrical signals and their functions are referred to by four different systems: pin number, EIA designation, CCITT designation, and abbreviation of signal description. The following paragraphs provide information about the electrical signals most encountered when interfacing a DTE terminal to a DCE device. Fortunately, the full set of RS-232 signals is rarely used, so we are able to overlook numerous signals without worry.

Pin 1 is referenced by the EIA as AA, by the CCITT as 101, and this abbreviated GND. It serves as the chassis ground between the two devices, but, it should not be depended on for shock protection. However, this pin should definitely be connected at each end because opening in the chassis ground can cause problems that are very difficult to trace.

Pin 7 is referenced by the EIA as AB, by the CCITT as 102, and is abbreviated SG. It serves as the signal ground. Pin 7 is the reference for all other pins and completes the circuit for the flow of current.

Pin 1 and pin 7 are the only two ground pins. Both should be connected; however, in most devices, they are connected to the same ground in the equipment. Thus, it is usually possible to get by with only 1 of the 2 connected. If there are separate chassis and signal grounds, and if pin 1 is not wired and the ground at each device is at different potentials, current may flow through pin 7 and possibly interfere with data flow.

In version D of the RS-232 standard, pin 1 is defined as shield and should not be connected to the interface. In version D, pin 1 is used to permit shielding of the interface cable. Pin 7, the signal ground, is the only ground connection that should be made in the interface cable when using version D.

Pin 2 is referenced by the EIA as BA, by the CCITT as 103, and is abbreviated TD. This pin serves as the transmit data pin. All information sent via the RS-232 port comes out on this pin.

Pin 3 is referenced by the EIA as BB, by the CCITT as 104, and is abbreviated RD. This pin serves as the receive data pin. All data received via the RS-232 port comes in on this pin.

These descriptions are viewed from the DTE. DCE sends data on pin 3 and receives on pin 2. Thus, the DTE transmits on pin 2 and the DCE receives on pin 2, and the DCE transmits on pin 3, and the DTE receives on pin 3.

Pin 4 is referenced by the EIA as CA, by the CCITT as 105, and is abbreviated RTS. This pin serves as the request to send indicator. When the DTE has data to send, it asserts the RTS.

Pin 5 is referenced by the EIA as CB, by the CCITT as 106, and is abbreviated CTS. This pin serves as the clear to send indicator. The DCE asserts the CTS when it is able to receive data from the DTE. According to the standard, the CTS may be asserted only after receiving an RTS from the DTE.

Pin 6 is referenced by the EIA as CC, by the CCITT as 107, and is abbreviated DSR. This pin serves as the data set ready indicator. It is asserted as a response to the DTR signal and indicates that the DCE is ready for operation.

Pin 20 is referenced by the EIA as CD, by the CCITT as 108/2, and is abbreviated DTR. This pin serves as the data terminal ready indicator. The DTR indicates that the DTE is ready to send and receive data. The DTR is asserted whenever the DTE has data to send, or in some cases whenever the terminal is operating.

Pin 8 is referenced by the EIA as CF, by the CCITT as 109, and is abbreviated DCD. It serves as the data carrier detect (or just carrier detect) indicator. The DCE asserts this pin when the communications channel is ready. Many DTEs will not transmit or receive data unless this pin is asserted. In some cases, pin 8 is wired to pin 20, so it is always asserted.

When the RS-232C standard is properly implemented, data will not be transmitted unless the RTS, CTS, DSR, DTR, and DCD pins are asserted. There are many other RS-232C signals, 20 in all, but the ones listed here are the most commonly used.

Signal levels

RS-232 signal voltages are not compatible with those used by most computer circuitry, so an additional power supply is incorporated in RS-232 equipment to provide the necessary voltages. RS-232 signals are referenced to the pin 7 signal ground. The positive voltages can range from 5 to 25 V. On pins 2 and 3, a positive voltage indicates a logic 0 level. The negative voltages range from –5 to –25 V. On pins 2 and 3, a negative voltage indicates a logic 1 level. The polarities are reversed for the control-line logic levels, with a logic level 1 meaning the pin is asserted on. When transmitting, voltages of +12 and –12 V usually are used by most devices. When receiving, the positive voltage must be greater than 3 V and the negative voltage must be less than –3 V in order to be interpreted correctly by the receiving circuitry.

Cable configurations

The following section describes several examples of RS-232 cables for a variety of applications. They might be of help when you are wiring your own cables or attempting to diagnose problems with your cable and interface.

Minimum cable

In a minimum RS-232 cable, as few as 3 pins can be connected. This is very convenient for use in lengthy cable runs. Pins 1(GND), 2(TD), 3(RD), and 7(SG) are connected (Fig. D-1). If the signal and chassis ground are connected in the equipment, only one pin is necessary; pin 1 is usually chosen.

In order for this cable to work, the RTS/CTS and DSR/DTR pairs must be ignored. If a piece of equipment will not work unless a pin is asserted, just wire it directly to the voltage required. Software flow control must be used with this 3-wire cable. More on flow control will follow.

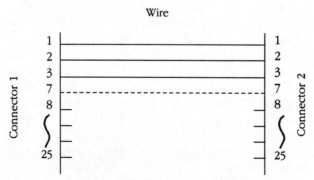

Fig. D-1. Diagram of an RS-232 minimum cable.

Full cable

The full cable should provide all connections necessary for most RS-232C applications. The following pins should be connected: pin 1 or pin 7, pin 2, pin 3, pin 4, pin 5, pin 6, pin 8, and pin 20 (Fig. D-2). This cable works in most situations and allows for hardware flow control.

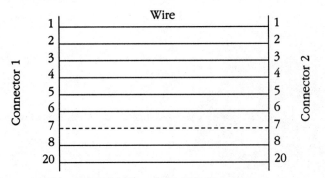

Fig. D-2. Diagram of an RS-232 full cable.

Null modem

A null-modem adapter allows two DTEs or DCEs to communicate with each other. Several pins must be reversed to allow the proper signals to reach the proper pins (Fig. D-3). If you recall from the signal descriptions of pins 2 and 3, a DTE transmits on pin 2 and receives on pin 3, and a DCE transmits on pin 3 and receives on pin 2. So when connecting two devices of a like type, these pins must be cross-connected so that one device's pin 2 is wired to the other device's pin 3 and the first device's pin 3 is wired to the other's pin 2. This configuration allows the two devices to transmit and receive on their proper pins.

The RTS of each device should be wired to its own CTS and to the DCD of the other device. This arrangement allows a request to send to receive an instant clear to send and also asserts the data carrier detect so the other device knows a transmission is coming. Additionally, the DTR and DSR pins must be cross-connected in

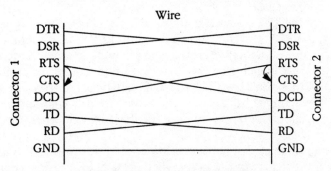

Fig. D-3. Diagram of an RS-232 null modem.

the same manner as the TD and RD pins to allow for proper signaling. The pin 1 and 7 grounds are wired straight through as usual.

A null-modem adapter is useful when transferring files between two computers or when connecting a computer to a printer that is wired as a DTE. It can be incorporated into a cable by switching the cable wires or through an adapter that is inserted into the cable. (Fig. D-4)

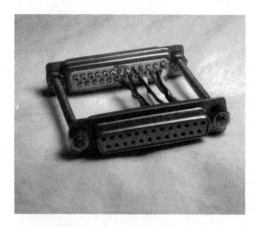

Fig. D-4. A null-modem adapter.

Flow control

Flow control is one of the potential problem areas of the RS-232 interface. *Flow control* is the process of stopping and starting the flow of data between devices. Flow control can be implemented in hardware, using the interface's signals, or in software. Under software flow control, the data flow is controlled independently of the physical interface.

The RS-232 standard was not designed for hardware flow control. Rather, it expected all flow control to be provided through software. One method of software flow control, known as Xon/Xoff, works by sending control characters over the physical interface. However, many computer manufacturers have attempted to control the flow of data between the devices through use of the RTS/CTS and DTR/DSR pairs. This has been accomplished with varying degrees of success with printers and modems, and has been carried over to packet radio TNCs and other amateur digital communications interfaces.

According to the RS-232 standard, the DCE is not allowed to drop the CTS until the DTE drops the RTS. The DCE should not drop its CTS at random for flow control. The proper use of the RTS/CTS pair is to allow the terminal to request use of the communication channel. However, hardware flow control using these pins is possible. Many TNCs don't have full RTS/CTS capability, so they can be used for flow control if the terminal will allow it, and most terminals will. Another approach, DTR/DSR flow control, works by turning off the DSR pin when the device can accept no more data.

There is no guarantee that hardware flow control will work, but it usually does. There are many problems that can occur when using hardware flow control, such as when to stop accepting data, what to do with a character that is partially sent when the device is told to stop sending, and when and at what character to resume sending. Check the terminal and TNC manuals carefully if you are planning to implement hardware flow control. For general use, it is usually best to stick with Xon/Xoff software flow control.

Nonstandard implementations

Another problem that can pop up when working with RS-232 compatible devices is nonstandard voltage levels. Instead of using the standard +12 and –12 V some equipment use voltages such as +5 and –5 or +5 and 0. Depending on how sensitive the RS-232 devices are to voltage levels, these nonstandard voltage levels might or might not work. In most cases they usually do.

Nonstandard pin assignments are yet another problem that can be encountered. Some TNCs have uses assigned to some pins other than as specified by the standard. These pins are usually not used for input/output (I/O) and are usually ones that are not commonly used by most devices. These pins might have strange voltages on them or might be used as special control lines. It is a good idea not to connect these pins unless you are certain they will not interfere with the data transmission or damage any equipment. Check the manuals for more specific information about a particular pin's function.

Limitations

Although the RS-232 standard has been a great aid over the years in standardizing serial data communication between devices, it does have many limitations. These limitations are usually not of concern to us as amateur radio operators, but you should consider them when working with RS-232 communications.

The maximum recommended cable length of 50 ft is not often found to be very limiting for amateur digital communications applications. The value of 50 ft is derived by dividing the maximum capacitance of 2,500 pF by the capacitance of a foot of cable, which is usually about 50 pF. The cable length can be increased through the use of shielded cable and in-line amplifiers.

The fact that the voltages used by RS-232 are not the same as those used to power most computer components requires the addition of another power supply. RS-232 utilizes what is known as an unbalanced ground. There is only one signal ground for all the pins, and a difference in ground potential at each end can change the allowable voltage detection range. As a result, signal detection errors can occur.

Despite these drawbacks, the RS-232 standard is fine for limited-distance, medium-speed applications such as microcomputer communications.

Wiring cables

Wiring your own RS-232 cables can save you a great deal of money over the price of a completed cable, and you can modify the cable to meet your own needs very easily. There are 3 main decisions to be made when wiring RS-232 cables: connector type, cable type, and number and type of pins.

The most common RS-232 connector is the DB-25, which comes in several varieties. You must first determine whether your equipment needs male or female connectors. The male connector is known as DB-25P (plug), and the female connector is known as DB-25S (socket). Each plug comes in two varieties: solder type and friction type.

With the solder type, individual wires are soldered to each needed pin. The cable can be composed of individual wires, usually a 4- to 5-wire ribbon cable or 4-wire telephone cable. Hoods are protective covers designed to fit over the back of the solder type DB-25 connector and provide a convenient handhold for plugging and unplugging the connector.

The friction type, also called an *insulation displacement* connector, is for use with ribbon cable, usually 25 wire. The cable is placed in a slot on the back of the connector, and the connector is compressed. Connector pins puncture the ribbon cable's insulation and make contact with the wires. Friction connectors provide a convenient means to wire all 25 pins quickly.

When you are constructing a cable, it is a good idea to always add an extra foot or so of cable. This arrangement makes rearranging the station much easier by not tying the TNC down to one particular location.

Conclusion

The RS-232C and RS-232D standards can be a pain to work with and diagnose if they are not working properly. In most cases, however, the interface works fine the first time. If you already have an RS-232 connection to a modem or other device, simply substitute the TNC (or whatever device you are using) for that device and everything should work fine.

If you have problems with an RS-232 interface, it is important to determine whether the interface cabling, the TNC, or the terminal's hardware and/or communications software is at fault. If the fault is isolated to the interface cabling, the information in this appendix should make finding and solving the problem a little easier.

Operating frequencies

IN THE UNITED STATES, AMATEUR RADIO DIGITAL COMMUNICATIONS OCCURS ON A variety of frequencies. The most common frequencies are listed in this appendix.

RTTY/AMTOR

80 m	3.600–3.650 MHz
40 m	7.050–7.100 MHz
20 m	14.070–14.110 MHz
15 m	21.075–21.100 MHz
10 m	28.075–28.100 MHz

SSTV

80 m	on or about 3.845 MHz
40 m	on or about 7.171 MHz
20 m	on or about 14.230 MHz
15 m	on or about 21.340 MHz
10 m	on or about 28.680 MHz

Packet

HF

HF operation usually conforms to the Bell 103 standard. However, the frequency of the tone pairs sometimes varies between units. Therefore, it might be necessary to tune slightly above or below the given frequencies. The frequencies given are the LSB carrier frequency with TAPR tone pairs (1,600 Hz and 1,800 Hz). HF operation takes place on a variety of frequencies, with 14.103 MHz being the most popular.

Band	Frequency
80–m	3.607 MHz
40–m	7.093 MHz
30–m	10.147 MHz
20–m	14.103 MHz
	14.105 MHz
	14.109 MHz
10–m	28.102 MHz

Note: HF packet operation also occurs on standard RTTY frequencies.

VHF

VHF operation usually conforms to the Bell standard. The vast majority of VHF packet activity takes place on 145.01 MHz. VHF packet operation occurs on unusual frequencies in some areas of the country for a variety of reasons.

Band	Frequency	Notes
2–m	145.01 MHz	Nationwide
	145.03 MHz	Nationwide
	145.05 MHz	Nationwide
	145.07 MHz	Nationwide
	145.09 MHz	Nationwide
	145.36 MHz	Southern CA
	146.745/.145 MHz	
	147.555 MHz	Southern and Central IL, IO, and east MS.
	145.70 MHz	Denver, CO
	145.57 MHz	Dallas, TX
	146.13/.73 MHz	Tucson, AZ
	146.13/.73 MHz	Atlanta, GA
1.25–m	223.40 MHz	Nationwide
	223.42 MHz	Local
	223.44 MHz	Local
	223.46 MHz	Local
	223.48 MHz	Local

Microsat frequencies and modes

Satellite	Uplink freq.	Downlink freq.	Mode
UO–14 UoSAT OSCAR 14	145.975 MHz	435.07 MHz	1,200 bps AFSK (FM)
UO–15 UoSAT OSCAR 15	N/A	435.12 MHz	1,200 bps AFSK (FM)

Satellite	Uplink freq.	Downlink freq.	Mode
AO–16	145.90 MHz	437.025 MHz	1,200 bps
AMSAT OSCAR 16	145.92 MHz	437.050 MHz	PSK AX.25
	145.94 MHz	2401.10 MHz	
	145.96 MHz		
DO–17	N/A	145.825 MHz	1,200 bps
DOVE OSCAR 17		2401.20 MHz	AFSK AX.25
			(FM) and digitized
			voice
WO–18	N/A	437.075 MHz	1,200 bps
WEBBERSAT OSCAR 18		437.100 MHz	PSK AX.25
LO–19	145.84 MHz	437.125 MHz	1,200 bps
LUSAT OSCAR 19	145.86 MHz	437.150 MHz	PSK AX.25
	145.88 MHz		
	145.90 MHz		

Appendix F

Sources

THIS APPENDIX CONTAINS THE ADDRESSES OF ORGANIZATIONS, COMPANIES, AND publications mentioned in this book. This appendix is segmented into several different areas—digital communications organizations, standards organizations, publications, and companies—to simplify locating a particular subject.

Digital communications organizations

The following organizations publish newsletters and promote activity.

AMRAD
Amateur Radio Research and Development Corp.
P.O. Drawer 6148
McLean, VA 22106

AMSAT
The Amateur Satellite Corp.
850 Silgo #601
Silver Spring, MD 20910

ARRL
American Radio Relay League
225 Main St.
Newington, CT 06111

Standards organizations

Write to the following organizations for information on specific standards.

CCITT
International Telecommunications Union
General Secretariat
Sales Service
Place de Nation
CH 1211
Geneva 20
Switzerland

or

United Nations Bookstore
Room 32B
UN General Assembly Building
New York, NY 10017

EIA
EIA Engineering Department
Standard Sales
2001 Eye St., N.W.
Washington, D.C. 20006

ISO
ISO Central Secretariat
Case Postale 56
1211 Geneva 20
Switzerland

Publications

The following publications are good sources of information on amateur radio digital communications.

AMRAD Newsletter
5829 Parakeet Dr.
Burke, VA 22015

CQ Magazine
76 North Broadway
Hicksville, NY 11801

Communications Quarterly—
The Journal of Communications Technology
76 North Broadway
Hicksville, NY 11801

Digital Digest
4063 North Goldenrod Rd.
Winter Park, FL 32792

Gateway
ARRL
225 Main St.
Newington, CT 06111

The Packet
VADCG
9531 Odlin Rd.
Richmond, BC V6X1E1
Canada

Packet Status Register
TAPR
P.O. Box 22888
Tucson, AZ 85734

QST
ARRL
225 Main St.
Newington, CT 06111

Spec-Com
P.O. Box H
Lowden, IA 52255

73 Magazine
WGE Center
Peterborough, NH 03458

Companies

The following companies were mentioned in this book.

AEA
Advanced Electronic Applications
2006 196th SW
Lynnwood, WA 98036

BILL ASHBY AND SON
P.O. Box 332
Pluckemin, NJ 07978

DRSI
Digital Radio Systems, Inc.
2065 Range Rd.
Clearwater, FL 34625

GLB ELECTRONICS
151 Commerce Pkwy.
Buffalo, NY 14224

HAPN
Box 4466, Station D
Hamilton, Ontario
Canada L8V 457

HEATHKIT
Amateur Radio Department
Benton Harbor, MI 49022

L.L. GRACE COMMUNICATIONS
41 Acadia Dr.
Voorhees, NJ 08043

KANTRONICS
1202 East 23rd St.
Lawrence, KS 66044

MFJ ENTERPRISES
921 Louisville Rd.
Starkville, MS 39759

MICROLOG
18713 Mooney Dr.
Gaithersburg, MD 20879

PAC-COMM PACKET RADIO SYSTEMS
3652 West Cypress St.
Tampa, FL 33607

RICHCRAFT ENGINEERING
One Wahmeda Industrial Park
Drawer 1065
Chautauqua, NY 14722

S. FINE SOFTWARE
P.O. Box 6037
State College, PA 16801

SOFTWARE 2000
1127 Hetrick Ave.
Arroyo Grande, CA 93420

TAPR
P.O. Box 22888
Tucson, AZ 85734

Appendix G

Introduction
to amateur radio

THIS APPENDIX IS INCLUDED FOR THOSE READERS WHO ARE NOT FAMILIAR WITH the amateur radio service. Digital communications is but a small part of the world of amateur radio. Amateur radio is a worldwide hobby that provides many services to the individuals and countries that encourage its growth. There are more than 1 million licensed amateur radio operators, including more than 400,000 in the United States.

Introduction

Amateur radio can be defined as radio communications between licensed stations without financial remuneration. Amateur radio operators have a wide variety of communications modes available for their use. The major modes in use today include Continuous Wave (CW), also called Morse code; Single Side Band (SSB)—voice; frequency modulation (FM)—voice; television, both fast and slow scan; radioteletype (RTTY); and packet. Communications can be by line-of-sight, ionosphere reflection, satellite, or more exotic modes such as moonbounce and meteor scatter.

Radio amateurs worldwide are authorized to operate on certain frequencies, just as commercial and government stations are. The frequency space occupied by amateur radio is very valuable, and the use of this space would be welcomed by commercial users and governments. Amateur radio justifies its uses of these frequencies by providing emergency communications and contributing to the development of new communications techniques. Packet radio fits right in here.

In the United States, a license issued by the FCC is required to operate an amateur radio station. Several grades of licenses are available. Each increase in license grade provides additional capabilities and requires the user to pass more difficult tests. These tests ensure that the operators are proficient enough to operate a station in the modes allowed.

Licenses

Licenses, capabilities, and testing vary from country to country. Five amateur radio licenses are available in the United States. Following is a brief summary of the elements tested and the capabilities each offers.

Novice   The Novice license is probably the easiest license to obtain. Novice privileges have been expanded to include voice and digital communications privileges on one HF band and several VHF and UHF bands, in addition to the previously permitted CW operation on the HF bands. The testing is relatively simple: Morse code at 5 words per minute (WPM), operating techniques, and basic electronic and radio theory.

Technician   The Technician class license is now composed of two classes. The lowest grade of Technician does not require any knowledge of the Morse code and provides full VHF and UHF privileges. The Codeless Technician was designed as an alternative entry license for those who do not wish to learn Morse code. To obtain the Codeless Technician, an applicant must pass both the Novice and Technician written tests, but does not have to take the 5 WPM code test.

The regular Technician license allows all the capabilities of a Novice plus full VHF and UHF capabilities. The test consists of the Novice elements (the Novice written and 5 WPM code tests) plus the Technician written test.

General   The General class license allows all the capabilities of a Technician, as well as increased operating capabilities on certain HF frequencies. The testing is the same as the Technician, with the exception of a 13 WPM Morse code test. The General class is the most popular license in the United States.

Advanced   The Advanced class license allows all the capabilities of a General, plus additional HF frequency privileges. The testing is the same as the General, with the exception of a higher-level theory test.

Extra   The Extra class license is the highest class of license available. It offers all the capabilities of the Advanced class plus the highest level of HF frequency operating privileges. The testing includes all the theory elements of the Advanced class, as well as another high-level theory test and a 20 WPM Morse code test.

Callsigns

Every licensed operator is assigned a unique callsign. New callsigns in the United States have a different format for each license class. In the case of an upgrade, the amateur may opt to keep his or her callsign from a lower-level license. Currently issued Novice callsigns are in the format of *XX#XXX*; Technician and General are *X#XXX*; Advanced is *XX#XX*; and Extra is *X#XX* or *XX#X* (where *X* indicates a letter and *#* a number). All United States callsigns can be identified by their prefix; always begin with N, K, A, or W.

The number in the callsign represents the district in which the license was issued. The United States is divided into numbered districts (0 to 9). When a licensee moves permanently to another district, he or she may keep his or her present callsign or apply for a new one with the new district number. The new callsign will not contain the same alphabetical characters as the old callsign, since new callsigns are issued in alphabetical order.

Conclusion

Amateur radio is a diverse hobby. I have not attempted to fully describe it in the limited space available here. For more information, contact the ARRL; their address is listed in appendix F. Also, look for an amateur radio magazine (such as *CQ* or *73*) on the newsstand. Check to see if there are any amateur radio equipment dealers nearby that you could visit.

Bibliography

THIS SECTION OF THE BOOK CONTAINS A SIZABLE LISTING OF BOOKS, PROCEEDINGS, papers, and articles dealing with amateur radio digital communications in some way. I have not attempted to compile a comprehensive listing of all the published material on amateur radio digital communications. With so many listings, it would be very difficult for you to select those works that would be of most interest to you without much time spent locating and examining each of them. Rather, I have selected material that reinforces and expands the concepts presented in this book, as well as material that I found helpful preparing this book. Of course, the standard references as established by members of the amateur radio digital communications community are also included.

Books

ARRL. *ARRL Amateur Radio Computer Networking Conferences.* Newington, CT: ARRL.

—— *The ARRL Handbook for the Radio Amateur.* Newington, CT: ARRL.

Davidoff, Martin K2UBC. *The Satellite Experimenter's Handbook.* Newington, CT: ARRL, 1984.

Folts, Harold C. and Harry R. Karp, ED. *Data Communications Standards.* New York: McGraw-Hill, 1979.

Friend, George E., et al. *Understanding Data Communications.* Dallas: Texas Instruments, 1984.

Green, Jr. Paul E., Ed. *Computer Network Architectures and Protocols.* New York: Plenum Press, 1982.

Grubbs, Jim K9EI. *Get ***CONNECTED to Packet Radio.* Springfield, IL: Q-Sky, 1986.

——— *The Digital Novice.* Springfield, : Q-Sky, 1987.

———*Digital Communications with Amateur Radio.* Richardson, TX: Master Publishing, 1988.

Horzepa, Stan WA1LOU. *Your Gateway to Packet Radio.* Newington, CT: ARRL, 1987.

Lancaster, Don. *TV Typewriter Cookbook.* Indianapolis: Howard W. Sams and Co., 1976.

Mayo, Jonathan L. KR3T. *The Packet Radio Handbook - 2nd Edition.* Blue Ridge Summit, PA: TAB Books, 1989.

Rouleau, Robert VE2PY and Ian Hodgson VE2BEN. *Packet Radio.* Blue Ridge Summit, PA: TAB Books, 1981.

Seyer, Martin D. *RS-232 Made Easy: Connecting Computers, Printers, Terminals, and Modems.* Englewood Cliffs, NJ: Prentice-Hall, 1984.

Tanenbaum, Andrew S. *Computer Networks.* Englewood Cliffs, NJ: Prentice-Hall, 1981.

Articles and papers

Abrams, Clay K6AEP. "From TUs to Communications Processors." *QST.* April 1988: 19–21.

Adams, W. Max W5PFG. "Briefly Speaking: Basic Amateur Radio Packet Radio." *CQ.* November 1985: 13–20.

Bishop, Jeffrey N7FDS. "Seeing Packet Radio with Different Eyes." *73.* August 1986: 48–49.

Borden, David W. K8MMO and Paul L. Rinaldo W4RI. "The Making of an Amateur Packet-Radio Network." *QST.* October 1981: 28–30.

Churchward, Budd WB7FHC. "Packet Radio: Getting Started." *World Radio.* April 1986, 6.

Davey, J.R. "Modems." *Proceedings of the IEEE.* Vol 60 1972. 1284–1292.

Flammer, George WB6RAL. "Survival Training for Mountaintop Digipeaters." *73.* August 1986: 68–73.

Forsyth, Mike KB7DCJ. "The Inside Story of the PK-232." *QST.* May 1988: 30–33.

Henry, Bill K9GWT. "Adapting Your Station for RTTY." *CQ.* February 1986: 22–24.

———"New AMTOR Mode!" *CQ.* November 1989: 36–40.

Hodgson, Ian VE2BEN. "An Introduction to Packet Radio." *Ham Radio*. June 1979: 64–67.

Hutton, Louis K7YZZ. "Connect Alarm!" *73*. August 1986: 66.

Johnson, Lyle WA7GXD. "Join the Packet Radio Revolution." *73*. September 1983: 19–24.

———"Join the Packet Radio Revolution—Part II." *73*. October 1983: 20–31.

———"Join the Packet Radio Revolution—Part III." *73*. January 1984: 36–44.

Karn, Phil KA9Q. "Beyond Level Two." *73*. August 1986: 74–78.

Lamb, Mike N7ML. "RFI and Computers in the Shack." *CQ*. November 1987: 66–68.

Langner, John WB2OSZ. "Precision Packet Tuning." *73*. August 1986: 40–47.

Macassey, Julian N6ARE. "Computers and Hams." *World Radio*. February 1986: 26–27.

Markoff, John. "Bulletin Boards in Space." *Byte*. May 1984: 88–94.

Martinez, J.P. G3PLX. "Amtor, an Improved Error-Free RTTY System." *QST*. June 1981: 25–27.

Mayo, Jonathan L. KR3T. "Portable RTTY." *CQ*. November 1985: 46–47.

———"An Amateur Packet Radio Primer: Part I—Introduction." *CQ*. November 1986: 11–17.

———"An Amateur Packet Radio Primer: Part II—Equipment." *CQ*. December 1986: 55–60.

———"An Amateur Packet Radio Primer: Part III—Operating Packet Radio." *CQ*. January 1987: 18–20.

———"An Amateur Packet Radio Primer: Part IV—Bulletin Board Operation." *CQ*. February 1987: 30–33.

———"Amateur Packet Radio. Who Needs It? You Do!" *CQ*. November 1988: 11–17.

———"Amateur Packet Radio Networking and Protocols, Part 1." *Ham Radio*. February 1988: 33–38.

———"Amateur Packet Radio Networking and Protocols, Part 2." *Ham Radio*. March 1988: 56–64.

———"Amateur Packet Radio Networking and Protocols, Part 3." *Ham Radio*. April 1988: 41–45.

———"Understanding the RS-232 Standard." *CQ*. November 1988: 32–36.

———"Don't Forget RTTY." *CQ*. January 1989: 36–39.

Morrison, Margaret KV7D, and Dan Morrison KV7B. "Amateur Packet Radio: Part 1." *Ham Radio*. July 1983: 14–18.

Morrison, Margaret KV7D, and Dan Morrison KV7B, and Lyle Johnson WA7GXD. "Amateur Packet Radio: Part 2." *Ham Radio.* August 1983: 18–29.

Newland, Paul AD7I. "An Introduction to AMTOR." *QST.* July 1983: 11–13.

——— "A User's Guide To AMTOR Operation." *QST.* October 1985: 31–34.

Pearce, Jon WB2MNF. "So You Want To Be A Sysop?" *73.* August 1986: 50–55.

Popiel, Glen WA4FTZ. "Packet Radio Operating Tips." *World Radio.* April 1986: 28.

Price, Harold NK6K. "What's all this Racket about Packet?" *QST.* July 1985: 14–17.

——— "A Closer Look at Packet Radio." *QST.* August 1985: 17–20.

——— "Birds 'N' Bauds." *73.* August 1986: 58–64.

——— "And If That Wasn't Enough . . ." *73.* August 1986: 80–85.

Reedy, Gwyn W1BEL. "A Packet Primer." *73.* August 1986: 28–32.

Rogers, Buck K4ABT. "Starter Packet." *CQ.* November 1989: 11–21.

——— "The Newcomer's Guide To AMTOR." *CQ.* November 1989: 51–55.

Rouleau, Robert T. VE2PY. "The Packet Radio Revolution." *73.* December 1978: 192–193.

Sternberg, Norm W2JUP. "How To Make Friends at 1200 Baud." *73.* August 1986: 34–39.

Winter, Patty N6BIS. "Packet Radio in Emergency Communications." *QST.* September 1986: 53–57.

Zorpette, Glen. "The High-Tech Hobbyhorse." *IEEE Spectrum.* May 1985: 96–98.

Glossary

ACK Shortened form for acknowledgment. Sent by the destination station to the originating station to indicate the successful reception of a frame. *See* NAK.

address **1.** The specific designation given to each station on the network for identification purposes. In AX.25, the address consists of the amateur station's callsign plus a substation identifier ranging from 0 to 15. **2.** The first field of an HDLC frame following the initial flag and containing the addresses of the originating and destination stations. In AX.25, the address field may include digipeaters. *See* SSID.

AFSK Acronym for audio frequency shift keying, a method of modulation in which the RF carrier remains constant and an audio tone is shifted in frequency. When used on an SSB transmitter, it cannot be differentiated from FSK.

ALOHA Also ALOHANET, an early packet radio network set up at the University of Hawaii in 1970 for research and development of packet radio communications. *See* menehune.

AMTOR Acronym for AMateur Teletype Over Radio, an advanced form of RTTY usually operated on the HF bands.

analog A signal that varies in a continuous manner (i.e., voice, music, and voltage and currents that vary in a continuous manner). *See* digital.

ANSI Acronym for American National Standards Institute, the principal standards development organization in the United States. *See* CCITT; EIA; ISO.

Answer Back The response to a WRU request.

application layer Level 7 of the OSI/RM; contains user software.

ARQ AMTOR Mode A; error-checked communications between two stations.

argument A variable expression that follows a command.

ASCII Acronym for American Standard Code for Information Interchange. Also

USASCII. A 7-bit code established by ANSI to achieve compatibility between digital devices.

asynchronous   Also called *start-stop* transmission. Of or referring to digital signals that are sent as groups of a specified length with start- and stop-bit indicators at the beginning and end of each group. Usually used when time intervals between transmitted groups may be uneven. *See* synchronous.

AX.25   Amateur packet radio protocol version of the X.25 protocol. Usually used in reference to the data link layer protocol used by most amateur packet stations.

baud   A unit of signaling speed equal to the number of discrete signal events per second. Baud is the same as bps only if each signal event represents exactly one bit.

Baudot code   Also called *Murray code,* a 5-level code for the transmission of data in digital form. Named for Emile Baudot. Baudot code is usually found in older teleprinters.

BBS   Acronym for Bulletin Board System; also called *CBBS, PBBS,* and *Mailbox.* An automated computer system which can be controlled from a remote location. Usually capable of sending and receiving messages and files.

Bell 103   Of or referring to a modem standard with a 200 Hz shift (1,070 Hz, 1,270 Hz) operating at 300 baud. Used for HF amateur packet radio operation.

Bell 202   Of or referring to a modem standard with a 1,000 Hz shift (1,200 Hz, 2,200 Hz) operating at 1,200 baud. Used for VHF FM amateur packet radio operation.

BER   Acronym for bit error rate.

binary   A number system based on the powers of 2. The only characters are a "0" and a "1." Binary digits are easily transmitted and stored in electronic equipment. *See* bit; hex; and octal.

bipolar keying   A technique in which a binary "1" is represented by a positive pulse, and a binary "0" by a negative pulse. Bipolar keying is the system used by NRZI on amateur packet radio. *See* NRZ; Manchester; and encoding technique.

bit   Abbreviation for binary digit; either a "0" or a "1."

bit stuffing   The addition of a binary "0" following all sequences of 5 binary "1"s in the data transmission to avoid the accidental occurrence of a flag. The added binary "0" is removed by the receiving station.

BOP   Acronym for bit-oriented protocol, a protocol in which control and data consume only as many bits as needed and there is no minimum binary grouping. *See* COP.

buffer   Memory space set aside for the temporary storage of data until recalled, processed, or permanently stored.

bus network   A network configuration in which all nodes are on the same channel and may communicate with each other directly, providing they are within range.

byte   A grouping of 8 bits. *See* nybble; octet.

CCITT   Acronym for "Comite Consultatif Internationale de Telegraphique et Telephonie, an international standards committee that establishes international communications standards. *See* ANSI; EIA; ISO.

checksum   The numeric result of a CRC, sent within a frame as the FCS.

collision   The condition that occurs when two or more stations transmit at the same time, or when one or more stations transmit while another station is transmitting. A collision might destroy one or more of the transmissions, depending on the relative strength of the signals and the sensitivity of the receivers.

command   A string of characters recognized and acted upon by a device.

command set   A subset of the user interface consisting of all available commands and parameters. It may be organized by group, function, or alphabetically.

connection   The condition of having established communications between two stations.

contention   A condition in which two or more stations try to transmit at the same time.

control character   A special character recognized by the receiver (usually a computer) as having a special meaning. Usually sent by pressing a control key and the appropriate character on the keyboard. Control characters are written in the abbreviated form as CRTL or CTL. For example, CTRL-C: break, CTRL-M: carriage return.

COP   Acronym for character oriented protocol, a protocol in which all information must be sent as characters of a specified length. *See* BOP.

CPU   Acronym for central processing unit, the "brains" of a computer. Responsible for directing the flow of data throughout the computer.

CRC   Acronym for cyclic redundancy check, an error-detection scheme in which a check character is generated by dividing the entire numeric binary value of a block of data by a generator polynomial expression. The CRC value is sent along with the data, and at the destination station, the CRC is recomputed from the received data. If the received CRC value matches the one generated from the received data, the data is considered errorfree. *See* FCS; checksum.

CSMA/CD   Acronym for Carrier Sense Multiple Access with Collision Detection, the system used in amateur packet radio to handle time-division multiplexing of the channel and contention. Each station monitors the channel and only transmits when the channel is clear. The absence of an ACK from the destination station indicates that a collision may have occurred, and the transmission is re-sent after waiting a random time interval.

CTS   Acronym for clear to send in the RS-232 standard. Also referred to as Pin 5, CB by the EIA, and 106 by the CCITT.

data   The digital information that is being transmitted or received.

data link layer   Level 2 of the OSI/RM, which arranges bits into frames, establishes and maintains a link, and performs error detection and recovery. ISO HDLC is the most common level-2 protocol.

datagram   A type of packet networking in which each packet contains complete and extensive addressing and control information, allowing for variable routing at the expense of greater overhead. *See* virtual circuit.

DB-25   A series of 25-pin connectors commonly used in RS-232 interfacing applications.

DCD   **1.** An indicator that signals the presence of a signal. **2.** Acronym for data carrier detect in the RS-232 standard. Also referred to as Pin 8, CF by the EIA, and 109 by the CCITT.

DCE   Acronym for data communication equipment, a device capable of establishing, maintaining, and terminating a connection. The DCE also may have to handle signal conversion and coding. *See* DTE.

demodulation   The process of retrieving data from a modulated signal. *See* modulation and modem.

digipeater   A simplex packet repeater that stores an incoming packet, and, if so instructed, retransmits it. The digipeater does not retain a copy of the packet once sent or wait for an acknowledgment from the next node.

digital   Of or referring to a discrete or discontinuous signal whose various states are identified with specified values. *See* analog; RS-232; TTL.

DOS   Acronym for disk operating system.

downlink   A radio link originating at a satellite and terminating at a ground station. *See* uplink.

DSR   Acronym for data set ready in the RS-232 standard. Also referred to as Pin 6, CC by the EIA, and 107 by the CCITT.

dumb terminal   A communications terminal with only the basic capabilities necessary for communications, such as an input device, an output device, and a predefined I/O port. *See* smart terminal.

EBCDIC   Acronym for Extended Binary Coded Decimal Interchange Code, an 8-level character code developed by IBM and used primarily in its equipment. *See* ASCII; Baudot.

EIA   Acronym for Electronic Industries Association, a standards organization specializing in interface equipment. *See* ANSI; CCITT.

encoding technique   Also called *line coding, channel coding,* and *data format.* The system used to encode the digital data for transmission. *See* NRZ; NRZI; Manchester.

FAD   Acronym for frame assembler/disassembler. Often used interchangeably with PAD and TNC.

FCS   Acronym for frame check sequence, a CRC for a frame.

FDM   Acronym for frequency division multiplexing, a technique for distributing users over a number of separate channels; each channel may have different characteristics. *See* TDM; SDM.

FEC   AMTOR Mode B, the collective broadcast mode. A broadcast of data from one station to multiple stations. *See* SEL-FEC.

flag   A unique binary sequence used to delimit frames at the data link layer. In HDLC, the flag is 01111110. *See bit stuffing.*

flow control   The process of stopping and starting the flow of data between devices.

frame   A group of bits delimited by flags. It may contain control information and data.

FSK   Acronym for frequency shift keying, a method of frequency modulation in which the frequency varies. *See* AFSK; PSK.

full duplex   Of or referring to simultaneous two-way independent transmission in both directions on separate channels. *See* simplex; half duplex.

gateway   A device that retransmits received data in another format and/or on another channel.

half duplex A circuit designed for transmission in either direction on two separate channels, but not in both directions simultaneously. *See* full duplex; simplex.

hardware Physical equipment, as opposed to a program or protocol; for example, TNC board, computer, printer. *See* software.

HDLC Acronym for high-level data link controller, an ISO standard for the data link layer of the OSI/RM. *See* protocol.

header The collective components of a frame preceding the information component. The header of an AX.25 frame consists of an opening flag, the address field, and control information.

hex Abbreviation for hexadecimal, a number system based on the powers of 16. Characters are 0–9 and A–F. *See* binary; octal.

IC Acronym for integrated circuit.

I/O Acronym for input/output; used in reference to any system or function that deals with sending and receiving data.

IRS Acronym for information receiving station, the station in an AMTOR ARQ pair that is currently receiving.

ISO Acronym for International Standards Organization. *See* CCITT; EIA; ANSI.

ISS Acronym for information sending station, the station in an AMTOR ARQ pair that is currently sending.

landline Commonly, of or referring to a terrestrial cable link between two stations; usually used in reference to the telephone system.

LAPB Acronym for link access procedure balanced, a subset of HDLC in which each node is treated on an equivalent basis, each able to send commands and responses.

LCD Acronym for liquid crystal display, a display device commonly used in portable computers that contains a crystalline liquid whose optical properties change in the presence of an electric field to appear either light or dark.

level 1–7 Numerical designators for the OSI/RM levels as follows: level 1: physical layer; level 2: data link layer; level 3: network layer; level 4: transport layer; level 5: session layer; level 6: presentation layer; level 7: application layer.

Manchester Of or referring to an encoding technique similar to NRZI but differing because the transition from positive to negative or negative to positive occurs in the middle of the bit signaling period. Two types are Manchester I and Manchester II. *See* NRZ.

master The AMTOR station that originated an ARQ communication. *See* slave.

menehune The central node in the Aloha packet radio network.

modem Contraction for modulator/demodulator, a device that modulates transmitted signals and demodulates received signals. It serves as an interface between an analog communications system and digital devices.

modulation The process of adding a signal to a carrier to transmit information. Can be used in reference to voice communications, but refers to digital data in the context of packet radio. *See* demodulation and modem.

Monitor AMTOR Mode L, also called *Listen*; a receive-only mode with no error checking.

monitor mode A mode in which the TNC is instructed to forward all received packets to the terminal. The user usually specifies categories of packets to be displayed (i.e., to or from certain stations, digipeated packets, control packets).

MSK   Acronym for minimum shift keying, a modulation method similar to FSK in which the shift in hertz is equal to half the signaling rate in bps. *See* AFSK; FSK; PSK.

multiconnect   The ability of a packet station to connect with more than one station simultaneously.

multiplex   Of or referring to the process of dividing a communications medium so that many users can share it. *See* FDM; SDM; TDM.

NAK   Shortened form for a negative acknowledgment. *See* ACK.

network   An interconnection of computer systems, terminals, and communications facilities.

network layer   Level 3 of the OSI/RM, which deals with addressing, routing, multiplexing, and flow control. Two types of networks are virtual circuit and datagram.

network node   Also called a *packet switch*; a hardware system with a level-3 protocol designed to forward packets through the network to their destination. *See* datagram; virtual circuit.

node   A general term used to indicate the different stations in a packet network. Nodes may be terminal nodes, network nodes, station nodes, and others. *See* TNC and digipeater.

NRZ   Acronym for non return to zero, an encoding technique for binary digital signals in which a binary "1" is encoded as a positive pulse and a binary "0" as a negative pulse. When modulated, the positive pulse becomes the mark tone, and the negative pulse, the space tone. This is the encoding technique used in RTTY. *See* Manchester.

NRZI   Acronym for non return to zero inverted. An encoding technique for binary digital signals in which a binary "0" causes a change in signal level, while a binary "1" causes no change. This is the encoding technique in use in most amateur packet radio systems. *See* Manchester.

null   A blank; a meaningless character usually used to consume extra bit space or time.

null modem   An RS-232 interfacing device that switches several pins to allow DTEs or DCEs to communicate with devices of the same designation.

nybble   A group of 4 bits; one half of a byte. Represented by a single hex character.

octal   Of or referring to a number system based on the powers of 8. Characters are 0–7. *See* hex and binary.

octet   A group of 8 bits. *See* byte; nybble.

OSCAR   Acronym for Orbital Satellite Carrying Amateur Radio.

OSI/RM   Acronym for open systems interconnection reference model; a formal hierarchical identification of all network functions as established by the ISO.

overhead   Any information other than the actual data that is transmitted.

packet   A group of bits, including data and control elements, which is transmitted as a whole. Technically, a packet is not formed until the network layer; however, many refer to frame transmissions on the data link layer as packets.

packet controller   A hardware TNC with an on-board modem.

packet switch   A device that is used with a network layer protocol to forward (switch) data sent on the network to the next node. Packet switches acknowledge data sent to them and then wait for an acknowledgment from the next node. In most cases, individual users are not involved in selecting the routing used by the packet switches. *See* network node.

PACSAT   Contraction of packet satellite, a packet satellite designed by AMSAT that will feature a flying mailbox similar to terrestrial BBSs.

PAD   Acronym for packet assembler/disassembler; used interchangeably with TNC. *See* FAD; TNC.

padding   The addition of an extra character to a group of characters in order to reach a predefined amount.

parallel transmission   A method of transmitting data in which all bits of each bit grouping are transmitted simultaneously on separate channels. *See* serial transmission.

parameter   A variable stored for future reference.

parity   The addition of a noninformation bit to a group of bits, making the total number of binary "1"s in the group either even or odd, depending on the type of parity selected. This permits single-bit error detection in each group.

path   The sequence of channels, gateways, and repeaters used to transmit information from one node to another.

peripheral   Any device that can be connected to a computer system to extend its operating capabilities.

physical layer   Level 1 of the OSI/RM, concerned with electrical characteristics of the communications link. *See* modem; RS-232.

PLL   Acronym for phase locked loop, a circuit for synchronizing an oscillator with the phase of a signal.

polling system   A method of TDM in which each station is asked (polled) to determine if it has any traffic to send. *See* random access.

presentation layer   Layer 6 of the OSI/RM, which performs any code conversion, handles control data structure and display formats, and manages data interchange with peripheral storage devices.

propagation delay   The time lapse between the transmission and the reception of a signal on a radio link. Satellite delays tend to be longer than those of terrestrial links.

protocol   A formal set of rules that dictates the format, timing, and other parameters of message exchange between two or more devices.

PSK   Acronym for phase shift keying, a method of transmitting digital information in which the phase of the carrier is varied in accordance with the digital signal.

RAM   Acronym for random access memory, electronic memory that can be read from and written to. However, once power is removed, all stored data is lost. Some RAMs provide for battery backup to retain the data in case normal power is removed.

random access   Of or referring to a type of network in which stations may transmit at any time provided the channel is available. *See* polling system.

ring network   A network configuration in which each node is connected to two other adjacent nodes, one on each side. When the connections are complete, the path of connections will resemble a ring or circle. Each node may communicate directly only with the node immediately preceding and following it. All nodes serve as relay stations to allow for communications throughout the network.

ROM   Acronym for read only memory, electronic memory that may be read from but not written to. Data is permanently retained. Some ROMs, such as the EPROM, allow for occasional programming and erasure. Most ROMs can be erased with UV light, so the transparent opening is covered with a label or sticker to block all light.

RS-232   **1.** An EIA standard. The latest version is D. A common serial communications interface for computer peripherals. **2.** Of or referring to the voltage signaling levels in electronic equipment. Range is –25 to –5 and +5 to +25 V; +/– 12 and +/– 5 V are commonly used.

RTS   Acronym for request to send, in the RS-232 standard. Also referred to as Pin 4, CA by the EIA, and 105 by the CCITT.

RTTY   Contraction of radio teletype, direct printing digital radio communications.

RUDAK   A packet experiment designed by the West German affiliate of AMSAT and included on the Phase IIIC satellite.

SEL-CAL   A four- or seven-letter grouping that identifies each AMTOR ARQ station. Usually made up of letters from the operator's callsign.

SEL-FEC   AMTOR Mode S; also called *selective broadcast*. A single station broadcasting to receiving stations with matching Group Call codes.

SDLC   Acronym for synchronous data link control, an IBM data link protocol very similar to HDLC.

SDM   Acronym for space division multiplexing, a method of allowing multiple users to share a single communications channel by arranging the users so that they are not in each other's communications range. *See* FDM; TDM.

serial transmission   A method of transmitting data in which each bit is sent sequentially on a single channel. *See* parallel transmission.

session layer   Level 5 of the OSI/RM, which initiates and terminates communications through the network. It also handles network logon and authentication.

simplex   Of or referring to operation over a single channel in one direction at a time. *See* full duplex and half duplex.

slave   The AMTOR station that responded to a call from a Master station in ARQ.

smart terminal   A communications terminal with advanced capabilities (such as Xon/Xoff flow control, buffers, variable parameters, and echoing), in addition to those required for basic communications. *See* dumb terminal.

software   The programs and procedures that control the operation of hardware systems.

standard   An established procedure, model, or design that has gained widespread recognition and conformity. It can be developed by committee, industry, or popular usage.

star network   A network in which all user nodes are situated about a central node. All communications between user nodes must take place through the central node.

start bit   In asynchronous serial communications, the first bit in each bit group, which notifies the receiver that a bit group is coming.

stop bit   In asynchronous serial communications, the last bit in each bit group, which notifies the receiver that the bit group is ended.

SWL   Abbreviation for shortwave listening.

synchronous   Of or referring to transmission in which the data is transmitted at a fixed rate with the transmitter and receiver synchronized. This method eliminates the need for start and stop elements, which are used with asynchronous transmission.

TAPR   Acronym for Tucson Amateur Packet Radio, a nonprofit organization specializing in packet radio development.

TDM   Acronym for time division multiplexing, the sharing of a single communications channel between many users by allotting the channel to each user on a time basis. *See* multiplexing; FDM; SDM.

teleport   A gateway between a terrestrial station or network and a satellite.

teleprinter   A typewriterlike device with a mechanical system to change keypresses into electrical pulses for transmission. Received pulses are converted back to characters, which are printed on paper.

Teletype   A registered trademark of the Teletype Corporation referring to a brand of teleprinter. *See* teleprinter.

terminal   A dedicated communications device that usually has a keyboard, display device(s), and an I/O port. *See* dumb terminal; smart terminal.

throughput   The actual rate of transmission, usually in bps, taking into account switching times, retransmissions, and other delays.

TNC   Acronym for terminal node controller, a device that assembles and disassembles frames. It usually includes some form of a user interface and command set, and can be implemented in hardware or software. It is used in conjunction with a radio, modem, and terminal for packet radio applications. *See* node; PAD; FAD; packet controller.

toggle   To switch between one of two possible conditions.

token passing   A form of TDM in which a unique binary sequence is passed from node to node. Only the node with the token may transmit.

transponder   A device that receives radio signals in one segment of the frequency spectrum and repeats them on another segment of the spectrum.

transport layer   Level 4 of the OSI/RM, which arranges data in order in the event packets arrive out of order.

TTL   Acronym for transistor transistor logic, a logic standard that represents a binary 1 as +5 V and binary 0 as 0 V.

turnaround delay   The time period required for a station to switch between receive mode and transmit mode.

UART   Acronym for universal asynchronous receiver transmitter, a device, usually packaged as an IC, that transmits and receives asynchronous serial data. The transmitter accepts data in parallel format and outputs the data in serial format. The receiver accepts data in serial format and outputs the data in parallel format.

unipolar keying   A technique in which a binary 1 is represented by a pulse and binary 0 by the absence of a pulse. Unipolar keying's poor performance led to the development of bipolar keying.

uplink   A radio link originating at a ground station and terminating at a satellite. *See* downlink.

user interface   The interface between the user and the device being used. In packet radio, the procedures implemented to allow the user to communicate with the TNC. *See* command set.

VADCG   Acronym for Vancouver Amateur Digital Communications Group.

VADCG Protocol   An early level-2 protocol based on HDLC, developed by Doug Lockhart VE7APU for use in packet radio. It is no longer in widespread use. Now called the V-1 protocol. *See* AX.25.

VDT   Acronym for video display terminal.

virtual circuit   A type of packet networking in which a logical connection is established prior to the transfer of data, thus allowing for abbreviated addressing and lower overhead at the expense of routing flexibility. *See* datagram.

WRU   Acronym for who are you, a code that, when received, causes the station to transmit its Answer Back message.

Index